OXFORD
UNIVERSITY PRESS

Janet Hardy-Gould
James Styring

English
Plus

Workbook 3

OXFORD
UNIVERSITY PRESS

Great Clarendon Street, Oxford OX2 6DP

Oxford University Press is a department of the University of Oxford.
It furthers the University's objective of excellence in research, scholarship,
and education by publishing worldwide in

Oxford New York

Auckland Cape Town Dar es Salaam Hong Kong Karachi
Kuala Lumpur Madrid Melbourne Mexico City Nairobi
New Delhi Shanghai Taipei Toronto

With offices in

Argentina Austria Brazil Chile Czech Republic France Greece
Guatemala Hungary Italy Japan Poland Portugal Singapore
South Korea Switzerland Thailand Turkey Ukraine Vietnam

OXFORD and OXFORD ENGLISH are registered trade marks of
Oxford University Press in the UK and in certain other countries

ISBN: 978 0 19 474862 9   Workbook
ISBN: 978 0 19 474886 5   MultiROM
ISBN: 978 0 19 474878 0   Pack

Printed in Spain by Orymu, S. A.

This book is printed on paper from certified and well-managed sources.

ACKNOWLEDGEMENTS

Illustrations by: Rob Hancock p.5; David Oakley pp.94, 95, 96, 98, 99, 100, 101.

Cover photographs: Getty Images (Teens climbing rock/Ligia Botero/Photonica),
iStockphoto (Teens doing homework outdoors/Bart Coenders), Photolibrary
(School students with globe/Image Source), (Teens reading a map/Paul Viant &
Carrie Beecroft/White).

The publisher would like to thank the following for permission to reproduce photographs:
Alamy pp.4 (subway/Chad Ehlers), 7 (watching TV/Rubberball), 13 (fire/Jim
Pickerell/Stock Connection Blue), 18 (fire/Qrt), 18 (rubbish/PE Forsberg),
21 (playground/Sally and Richard Greenhill), 24 (*World of Warcraft*/Kathleen
Smith), 28 (*Second Life*/Friedrich Stark), 29 (downloading music/Stocksearch),
50 (protest/Martin Jenkinson), 53 (cake sale/MShieldsPhotos), 56 (*Dangerous
Liaisons*/Pictorial Press Ltd), 61 (bullying/Bubbles Photolibrary), 64 (auction/Trip),
67 (London Eye/Jon Arnold Images Ltd), 69 (postcards/ArkReligion.com); Arnos
Design Ltd p.66 (CD); BBC Photolibrary p.10 (*Mastermind* quiz show), (the news);
Construction Photography p.18 (pipeline); Corbis pp.7 (cooking/Canopy),
13 (Eyjafjallajökull volcano/Odd Stefan Thorisson/Nordicphotos), 34 (Penelope
Cruz/Andrea Comas/Reuters), (Andy Murray/Christophe Karaba/epa), 40 (test/
Corbis Yellow), 60 (Amazon Kindle/Dani Cardona/Reuters), 64 (gallery/Jose Luis
Pelaez); Dreamstime p.50 (charity collection/moneybusiness); Getty pp.9 (Kanye
West/Daniel Boczarski), 10 (sports commentator/David Stluka), 18 (ex.1 bottle
bank/David Woodfall), 20 (catwalk model/China FotoPress), 36 (Underage Festival/
Rosie Greenway), 39 (Cheryl Cole/Mike Marsland/WireImage), 50 (vet/Dean
Golja/Digital Vision), 64 (statue/Gary Yeowell/The Image Bank), (painter/LWA/
Dann Tardif/The Image Bank); iStockphoto pp.7 (film crew), 50 (form/spxChrome),
64 (painting/Claudia Dewald); ITV pp.7 (*Who Wants To Be A Millionaire?*); Jupiter
Images p.64 (museum/Image Source); Oxford University Press pp.4 (tiger/Corbis/
Digital Stock), 7 (cooking/Photodisc), (on phone/Stockbroker), (going to school/
Chris King), 10 (weather forecast/Stockbyte/George Doyle), 13 (dog/Photodisc),
16 (fridge/Mark Mason), 18 (ex. 4 woman recycling/Bananastock), 33 (gallery/
Photodisc), (dim sum/Sylvain Grandadam), (washing machine/Digital Vision/
Andrew Olney), 34 (footballer/Bilderlounge), 35 (guard/Iconotec), 37 (dancer/
Comstock). 40 (girl/Chris King), 42 (school pupils/Chris King), 43 (tennis balls/
Photodisc), 44 (student/Design Pics), 45 (exam/Digital Vision), 48 (boy on bicycle/
Image Source), 50 (library/Image Source); Photolibrary p.49 (cleaning up/
Jupiterimages); Rex Features pp.10 (*Family Guy* cartoon/TM and copyright 20th
Century Fox), (*The X Factor* talent show/Ken McKay/TalkbackThames), (*Parkinson*
chat show/Ken McKay), 32 (Daniel Radcliffe/Charles Sykes), 56 (*High School Musical*/
Disney Chan/Everett), 68 (vases/Ian McCarney); Shutterstock p.18 (polluted
river/Foment); Still Pictures pp.18 (man cutting down tree/Mark Edwards),
52 (tribe/Martin Harvey); Superstock p.50 (gardening/age fotostock); The Art
Archive p.65 (The Scream, 1893/Edvard Munch/Nasjonal Galleriet, Oslo); The
Kobal Collection pp.10 (*Night at the Museum* film poster/20th Century Fox Film
Corporation), 12 (*Lost*/Touchstone/ABC), 56 (*Quantum of Solace*/Columbia/Danjaq/
Eon), (*Three Ten to Yuma*/Tree Line Films/Relativity Media), (*Flags of our Fathers*/
Dreamworks SKG/Warner bros), (*The Bourne Ultimatum*/Universal/Jason Boland),
(*The Golden Compass*/New Line Cinema), 58 (*Spider-Man 3*/Marvel/Sony Pictures).

*Although every effort has been made to trace and contact copyright holders before
publication, this has not been possible in some cases. We apologise for any apparent
infringement of copyright and, if notified, the publisher will be pleased to rectify any
errors or omissions at the earliest possible opportunity.*

Contents

S ◦◦◦◦◦◦◦◦◦ Starter unit

VOCABULARY ◼ Adjectives

1 ⭐ Find pairs of opposite adjectives.

~~cheap~~ common noisy boring
clean easy far heavy quiet rare
safe dangerous powerful unhealthy
useless weak difficult dirty exciting
~~expensive~~ healthy light near useful

<u>cheap</u>	<u>expensive</u>
1 _____	_____
2 _____	_____
3 _____	_____
4 _____	_____
5 _____	_____
6 _____	_____
7 _____	_____
8 _____	_____
9 _____	_____
10 _____	_____
11 _____	_____

2 ⭐⭐ Complete the sentences with adjectives in exercise 1.

There aren't many tigers left in India now. They are **rare**_____.

1 Wash your hands! They're _____.
2 This box is _____. Can you help me lift it, please?
3 Is it _____ to your school?
   No, it's only three minutes from here.
4 This dictionary isn't very _____. I can't find the word 'platinum'.
5 I got 97% in the science test. It was _____.
6 Our dog is ill. Its legs are _____ and it can't walk.
7 I love this film. It's very _____!
8 I can't hear you! It's very _____.

3 ⭐⭐ Choose the correct answers to complete the text.

Tokyo

Tokyo is a huge city of more than 13 million people. It's _____, but the shops and restaurants are [1]_____. The streets are busy and [2]_____, but they're always very [3]_____. There isn't much crime in Tokyo. It's a really [4]_____ city.

Japanese is a [5]_____ language for foreigners to read and speak. Visitors to Tokyo often get lost because they can't read the signs.

The railway is a popular form of public transport in Tokyo. The underground is also very busy and workers sometimes push passengers onto the trains! There are a lot of cars as well. The pollution from Tokyo's traffic sometimes makes the air quite [6]_____.

   a light (b exciting) c powerful
1 a expensive b near c rare
2 a weak b noisy c heavy
3 a clean b near c useful
4 a far b common c safe
5 a safe b difficult c useless
6 a quiet b difficult c unhealthy

4 ⭐⭐⭐ Write examples for the adjectives.

expensive   <u>a rare painting, a sports car</u>
1 quiet _____
2 dangerous _____
3 powerful _____
4 unhealthy _____
5 difficult _____
6 useful _____
7 noisy _____
8 boring _____

LANGUAGE FOCUS ● Comparative and superlative adjectives • Present simple

Comparative and superlative adjectives

1 ★ Look at the table and choose the correct words.

New DVD reviews

Tom met Sally	Dog Police	The Scientists
€12.99	€8.99	€15.49
😊	😊 😊 😊	😊 😊
112 minutes	121 minutes	134 minutes

The Scientists **is more exciting than /** **isn't as exciting as** *Dog Police.*

1 *The Scientists* **is more expensive than /** **isn't as expensive as** *Tom met Sally.*

2 *Tom met Sally* **is longer than / isn't as long as** *The Scientists.*

3 *Tom met Sally* **isn't as cheap as / is cheaper than** *The Scientists.*

4 *Dog Police* **isn't as expensive as / is more expensive than** *Tom met Sally.*

5 *Tom met Sally* **is shorter than / isn't as short as** *Dog Police.*

6 *Dog Police* **isn't as exciting as / is more exciting than** *Tom met Sally.*

7 *Tom met Sally* **is more boring than / isn't as boring as** *The Scientists.*

8 *The Scientists* **is better than / isn't as good as** *Dog Police.*

2 ★★ Write superlative sentences about the DVDs.

(expensive) *The Scientists is the most expensive DVD.*

1 (cheap) _____

2 (short) _____

3 (long) _____

4 (exciting) _____
   _____

5 (boring) _____
   _____

6 (good) _____
   _____

Present simple

3 ★★ Write sentences and questions using the present simple.

he / go / to my school
He goes to my school.

1 they / not tidy / their room every day
   _____

2 Gina / wash up / every evening
   _____

3 I / not sleep / for eight hours every night
   _____
   _____

4 Harry / do / his homework once a week
   _____
   _____

5 they / drive / to work every morning
   _____
   _____

6 school / not finish / at two o'clock
   _____

7 you / have / breakfast every day / ?
   _____

8 your brother / go / to work / ?
   _____

4 ★★★ Answer the questions. Write complete sentences.

What time does school start?
School starts at eight o'clock.

1 Do you get the bus to school?
   _____

2 Where does your mum / dad work?
   _____

3 How often do you watch TV?
   _____

4 What time do you have breakfast?
   _____

5 Do you tidy your room every week?
   _____

6 How do you relax?
   _____
   _____

7 What do you do at weekends?
   _____
   _____

8 What time do you wake up on Saturdays?
   _____
   _____

1 ★ Find eight more routines. Write them in the order they happen every day for you.

O	S	H	G	O	S	H	T	H	R	E	D
S	C	H	O	O	L	S	T	A	R	T	S
K	P	O	S	I	A	N	G	V	I	D	O
O	O	G	E	T	U	P	E	E	V	O	S
O	O	T	B	T	R	G	T	B	E	H	G
L	L	O	K	O	W	D	T	R	A	O	O
S	F	O	S	R	A	T	H	E	T	M	T
W	L	G	A	H	K	H	E	A	L	E	O
A	N	W	I	W	E	G	B	K	T	W	S
T	I	A	N	S	U	M	U	F	G	O	L
C	S	J	K	U	P	E	S	A	M	R	E
H	Y	F	H	K	N	C	N	S	O	K	E
T	E	K	T	H	I	B	S	T	E	S	P
V	S	G	O	T	O	B	E	D	S	E	T

wake up _____

1 _____ 5 _____
2 _____ 6 _____
3 _____ 7 _____
4 _____ 8 _____

2 ★★ Complete the sentences using the words in the box.

> shopping   go x 2   do   ~~get up~~   have
> watch   plays   bed

I ___get up___ at seven o'clock.

1 My parents don't _____ to work on Sundays.
2 She _____ basketball every week.
3 They _____ TV in the evenings.
4 I _____ my homework after school.
5 I never _____ to sleep before nine o'clock.
6 Do you usually _____ breakfast?
7 We often go _____ after school on Mondays.
8 What time do you go to _____ ?

3 ★★ Look at the routines for the two days and complete the text. Use the correct form of the verbs.

Wednesday

7.00	get up!
8.30	get bus
9.00	school starts
3.30	school finishes
4.00	relax in park!
6.30	do maths homework ☹
8.00	watch TV
10.00	go to bed!

Thursday

7.00	get up!
8.30	get bus
9.00	school starts
3.30	school finishes
4.30	go shopping with Tina
6.00	do history homework
7.30	go on computer
10.00	go to bed!

My sister ___gets up___ at 7 a.m. and she
[1]_____ the bus to school at 8.30 a.m.
School [2]_____ at 9 a.m. and it finishes at
3.30 p.m. After school on Wednesdays, she
[3]_____ with her friends. On Thursdays,
she [4]_____ shopping in town. In the
evening, she [5]_____ her homework
and then she [6]_____ TV or goes on the
computer and chats with her friends. She
[7]_____ to bed at 10 p.m.

4 ★★★ Complete the text about your routine on a school day.

I ___get up___ at about [1]_____
in the morning. I [2]_____
breakfast with [3]_____.
School [4]_____ at
[5]_____, so I
[6]_____ to school at
[7]_____. My favourite class
is [8]_____. School finishes
at [9]_____ in the afternoon.
After school, I [10]_____.
I usually go to bed at [11]_____.

Present continuous

1 ⭐ **Choose the correct words.**

It's the weekend and we (**'re**) / **'s** relaxing.

1 They **aren't** / **isn't** watching the film.
2 What **'s** / **are** he doing?
3 He **are** / **'s** having breakfast.
4 I **'m** / **are** learning English.
5 Why **aren't** / **isn't** you tidying your room?
6 I **aren't** / **'m not** doing my homework now.

2 ⭐⭐ **Look at the photos and complete the sentences.**

Aron and Ben _are watching tv._

They _aren't doing their homework._

(watch TV / do their homework)

1 Dad _____.
He _____.
(cook / read)

2 Brad _____.
He _____.
(chat / sleep)

3 Erin and Luke _____.
They _____.
(go to school / have breakfast)

Present simple and present continuous

3 ⭐⭐ **Complete the phone conversation. Use the present simple or the present continuous form of the verbs in brackets.**

Mum Hi, Ollie. It's Mum. I _'m coming_
(come) home now.

Ollie OK, Mum.

Mum ¹_____ (you / study) for your important exam?

Ollie No. I ²_____ (chat) to Simon. We ³_____ (talk) about the exam.

Mum But you ⁴_____ (talk) to him every day.

Ollie No, we ⁵_____ (not chat) in class. We ⁶_____ (listen) to our teacher.

Mum Are you sure? What ⁷_____ (your sister / do) at the moment? ⁸_____ (she / do) her homework?

Ollie No, of course not, Mum. She never ⁹_____ (do) her homework. She ¹⁰_____ (watch) TV, I think!

4 ⭐⭐⭐ **Invent a daily routine for a famous person. Write four sentences about it. Imagine what he / she is doing at the moment and write two sentences.**

Lionel Messi always gets up late. He doesn't have

breakfast.

At the moment, he's having dinner in an expensive

restaurant.

_____
_____
_____
_____
_____
_____
_____
_____
_____
_____
_____
_____
_____
_____
_____

1 (★) Match sentence halves 1–9 with a–i.

1 Are there any good programmes   _d_
2 They use special cameras   ___
3 Homer Simpson is my   ___
4 This new TV series   ___
5 The first TV broadcast   ___
6 Can I change channels   ___
7 Their new television has got a   ___
8 The show had three million   ___
9 I didn't watch the last   ___

a really big screen.
b viewers last year.
c was in black and white.
d on TV this evening?
e to make 3D films.
f has 12 episodes.
g favourite character in *The Simpsons*.
h episode of the series.
i with this remote control?

2 (★★) Complete the definitions about TV.

A _broadcast_ is when they transmit a TV show.

1 They record TV shows with a _____ .
2 An _____ watches a show.
3 You can turn the TV on and off with a _____ .
4 An _____ is one of several parts of a story.
5 A _____ is a person in a story.
6 A _____ is a TV show.
7 When you watch TV, you see the picture on the TV _____ .
8 A _____ is a show with a lot of episodes.

3 (★★) Complete the dialogue with the words in the box.

> adverts   audience   cameras
> channels   presenter   show   ~~programme~~

Jess What do you think is the best _programme_ on TV?

Ryan I love *Who Wants to Be a Millionaire?* It's my favourite ¹_____ .
I always watch it! I was in the ²_____ two years ago. My seat was behind the two ³_____ so it was a bit difficult to see, but the ⁴_____ was really funny.

Jess Why do you love it?

Ryan It's exciting!

Jess What do you think is the worst thing on TV?

Ryan I hate the ⁵_____ ! I prefer ⁶_____ without them.

4 (★★★) Answer the questions. Write complete sentences.

How many channels have you got on your TV at home?
I've got eight channels on my TV at home.

1 What is your favourite TV show? Why?
_____

2 Which programmes do you never watch? Why?
_____

3 Which series do you usually watch?
_____

4 Who is your favourite character? Why? What is the actor's name?
_____

5 Do you like adverts? Why / Why not?
_____

6 Who uses the remote control a lot in your house?
_____

was, were, there was, there were

1 ★ Choose the correct words.

Who **was** / **were** the main characters in *Futurama*?

1 We **was** / **were** lucky. **There was** / **There were** two more episodes on the DVD.
2 Where **was** / **were** your camera?
3 Marc **was** / **were** tired, so he didn't watch the end of the show.
4 **Was** / **Were** there any good programmes on TV last night?
5 The first episode **weren't** / **wasn't** in 2009. It **was** / **were** in 2010.
6 The presenters **weren't** / **wasn't** on yesterday's programme.
7 How old **was** / **were** the participants?
8 **Were there** / **Was there** many people in the audience?

2 ★★ Write sentences. Use the affirmative (✓), negative (✗) or question (?) forms of *was* / *were* and *there was* / *there were*.

I / at school this morning ✗
I wasn't at school this morning.

1 there / two channels without adverts ✓
_____
_____

2 there / a new character in the show this week **?**
_____
_____

3 the remote control / next to the TV **?**
_____
_____

4 you / in the audience **?**
_____

5 there / a new presenter in this series ✗
_____
_____

6 it / a new series ✓
_____
_____

7 who / the participants in *Big Brother* **?**
_____
_____

8 there / many TV broadcasts in the 1940s ✗
_____
_____

Past simple

3 ★★ Complete the text using the past simple form of the verbs in brackets.

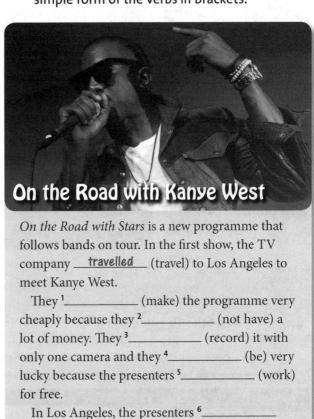

On the Road with Kanye West

On the Road with Stars is a new programme that follows bands on tour. In the first show, the TV company ___travelled___ (travel) to Los Angeles to meet Kanye West.

They **1**_____ (make) the programme very cheaply because they **2**_____ (not have) a lot of money. They **3**_____ (record) it with only one camera and they **4**_____ (be) very lucky because the presenters **5**_____ (work) for free.

In Los Angeles, the presenters **6**_____ (not stay) in a hotel. Instead, they **7**_____ (sleep) in a caravan.

During the show, Kanye **8**_____ (fly) in a private plane from city to city, but the TV company **9**_____ (follow) him in their car, with their caravan!

4 ★★★ Write questions for the answers.

Did you meet Kanye West?

Yes, we did. We met Kanye West in Los Angeles.

1 _____
We met him last month.

2 _____
Yes, we did. We liked him very much.

3 _____
After Los Angeles, we went to Las Vegas and then to San Francisco.

4 _____
No, we slept in a caravan.

5 _____
No, we didn't fly. We drove.

6 _____
We drove because the flights were expensive.

1 ⭐ Look at the photos. Complete the words.

c _artoon_

1 f_____

2 q_____

s_____

3 s_____

p_____

4 the n_____

5 t_____

s_____

6 w_____

f_____

7 c_____

s_____

2 ⭐⭐ Read the TV guide and label the programmes.

soap opera   ~~sitcom~~   reality show   documentary   drama   game show   the news   talent show

Channel 9		TV U2	
19:45	_sitcom_ **At the Office** More laughs with Harry's 'friends' at work. Harry does a funny dance at the office party.	19:45	¹ _____ **Birds of Panama** Can birds predict the weather? Join Monty Jones and the team in Panama.
20:15	² _____ **West Street** In today's episode, Sonia loses her job and Ali has problems with the police.	20.30	³ _____ **Dance-O-Rama** There are only three teams on the show now. Which team will leave tonight?
21:15	⁴ _____ **Open the box!** Will this week's participants open the right boxes and win £100,000?	21:15	⁵ _____ **Oliver Twist** A fantastic version of the famous Dickens story set in 1830s London. Episode 1 of 4.
22:00	⁶ _____ **Big Brother** Carol is cooking, but will the participants like the meal?	22:00	⁷ _____ **The World At Ten** All of today's main stories. Followed by the weather.

3 ⭐⭐ Complete the definitions.

A _sitcom_ is a type of comedy show.

1 A _____ is a show with moving drawings.
2 They ask lots of questions in a _____. The winner often gets a prize.
3 There are a lot of hospital scenes in a _____.
4 _____ often shows football matches.
5 You watch a _____ at the cinema.
6 A presenter interviews guests on a _____.

4 ⭐⭐⭐ What are your favourite television programmes? What type of programme is each one?

I love 'Match of the Day'. It's a sports programme.

1 _____
2 _____
3 _____
4 _____
5 _____
6 _____

Past continuous

1 ★ Complete the table with *was, wasn't, were* or *weren't*.

Affirmative		
I	__was__	watching a film.
You	__were__	enjoying the film.
He / She / It	¹_____	sleeping.
We / You / They	²_____	talking.

Negative		
I	__wasn't__	wearing a coat.
You	³_____	reading.
He / She / It	⁴_____	looking.
We / You / They	⁵_____	acting in the film.

Questions			
—	__Was__	I	sleeping?
Where	__were__	you	going?
What	⁶_____	he	doing?
—	⁷_____	she	listening?
Why	⁸_____	they	laughing?

2 ★★ Read the interview. Choose the correct answers.

> **CineMag** What _____ in Budapest? ¹_____ in a film?
> **Robert** No. I ²_____. I ³_____ a film.
> **CineMag** Wow! That's exciting! Was it difficult?
> **Robert** Yes. We ⁴_____ quickly because we didn't have much time. I ⁵_____ because I was so worried, but in the end my old friend Cameron helped me.
> **CineMag** Really?
> **Robert** Yes, he ⁶_____ in Bratislava. I called him and he agreed to help.

   a was you doing   **b** you were doing   (**c** were you doing)

1. **a** You were acting   **b** Were you acting   **c** You're acting
2. **a** wasn't   **b** was   **c** weren't
3. **a** was directing   **b** wasn't directing   **c** were directing
4. **a** are working   **b** weren't working   **c** were working
5. **a** were sleeping   **b** wasn't sleeping   **c** weren't sleeping
6. **a** were filming   **b** was he filming   **c** was filming

3 ★★★ Write questions. Think about what was happening at eight o'clock yesterday evening and write true answers.

you / read

Were you reading? Yes, I was reading a novel. / No, I wasn't. I was washing the dishes.

1. what / you / do
   _____
   _____
2. what / you / wear
   _____
   _____
3. who / you / talk to
   _____
   _____
4. what / your friends / do
   _____
   _____
5. what / your dad / do
   _____
   _____
6. your mum / cook
   _____
   _____

Past simple and past continuous

4 ★★ Complete the sentences. Use the past simple or past continuous form of the verbs in brackets.

Sylvia __was running__ (run) when she __dropped__ (drop) the DVDs.

1. While Steve _____ (watch) a documentary, he _____ (fall) asleep.
2. _____ you_____ (do) anything when I _____ (call)?
3. They _____ (not listen) when you _____ (ask) for the remote control.
4. _____ you _____ (see) your friends while you _____ (walk) to school this morning?
5. The film _____ (start) while I _____ (get) a drink.
6. The presenter _____ (come) in while the audience _____ (laugh).
7. I _____ (look) out of the window when Mum and Dad _____ (arrive) home.
8. We were _____ (drive) home when the accident _____ (happen).

1 ⭐ **Read the text. Tick ✓ the correct box.**

The text is about …

a ☐ an episode of *Lost*.

b ☐ the main actor in *Lost*.

c ☐ the series *Lost*.

ABC broadcast the first episode of *Lost* in 2004. The series started with a scene on a flight from Sydney, Australia, to Los Angeles, USA. The plane was flying over the Pacific Ocean when, suddenly, it crashed. There were 324 passengers on the plane and everybody thought they were dead. But in the mysterious world of *Lost*, 48 passengers survived.

The survivors landed on a small island and they worked together to find food. Every day, they waited for a ship or a plane, but help never arrived. While they were living on the island, they had a lot of scary experiences. In one episode, the survivors were walking in the jungle when they saw a huge polar bear. They discovered that other people were living on the island, but 'the Others' weren't friendly.

There was a flashback in every episode. These showed what the characters were doing before the plane crashed. One of the most interesting characters was the American doctor and leader of the group, Jack (played by Matthew Fox). The flashbacks explained a lot about the characters, but the island kept its secrets.

Audiences loved *Lost* because the plot was very unusual. The island was still a mystery when the series ended, after 114 episodes, in 2010.

2 ⭐⭐ **Read the text again. Find the words in the text and match them with the definitions.**

1 passengers   a people who don't die in an accident
2 survivors
3 leader   b people in a plane, car, or train
4 flashback   c a person who is in control of a group
5 plot   d the story in a film or show
                 e a scene that shows an earlier part of a story

3 ⭐⭐ **Complete the text with the words in the box.**

> Jack   Los Angeles   a̶ ̶p̶l̶a̶n̶e̶ ̶c̶r̶a̶s̶h̶   USA
> Pacific Ocean   Sydney   Matthew Fox

Lost is the story of the survivors of __a plane crash__ in the ¹_____. The flight started in ²_____ and the plane was flying to ³_____. ⁴_____ played a character called ⁵_____, a doctor from the ⁶_____.

4 ⭐⭐⭐ **Answer the questions. Write complete sentences.**

How many passengers lived after the crash?
__Forty-eight passengers survived.__

1 How did the passengers survive on the island?
_____
_____

2 What were the survivors doing when they saw the polar bear?
_____
_____

3 Who else was living on the island?
_____

4 How did the audience learn more about the characters?
_____
_____

5 Why was *Lost* popular?
_____
_____

6 When did the series end?
_____

Build your vocabulary

5 ⭐⭐ **Complete the sentences with the past simple form of the verbs in brackets.**

ABC __made__ (make) 114 episodes of *Lost*.

1 The show _____ (attract) a large audience.
2 The viewers _____ (love) this TV series.
3 The show _____ (win) a lot of prizes.
4 The final series _____ (show) the 'Man in Black'.
5 ABC _____ (broadcast) the last episode in 2010.

Language point: Time connectors

1 ★ Order the sentences.

Dog Rescues Man

a ☐

At first, the fire was small. Mr Salter rang to get help and he threw water on the fire to try to stop it.

b ☐

Finally, the firemen put the fire out and saved Mr Salter.

c ☐

Then Riley ran to get help. The firemen saw Riley and followed her to the fire and found Mr Salter.

d ☐ 1

The incident happened last Friday. Gavin Salter, 43, was at home with his dog, Riley, when a fire started in the kitchen.

e ☐

After a few minutes, the fire got bigger. The smoke made Mr Salter very ill. Riley tried to help him, but Mr Salter lay on the floor in the kitchen.

2 ★★ Read the text. Complete the sentences with one of the connectors in brackets.

Volcanic ash cloud

Eyjafjallajökull, a volcano in Iceland, started to erupt two weeks ago. ___At first___, (At first / While) people who lived near the volcano moved away from the area. **1**_____ (As soon as / Then) a lot of thick smoke started to come from the volcano. **2**_____, (While / Later) the wind changed direction, and a cloud of volcanic ash started to move south.

People were worried. They thought that the volcanic ash could break plane engines. **3**_____ (As soon as / While) the clouds arrived over northern Europe, the airports closed and nobody could fly. **4**_____ (While / Later) the European airports were closed, thousands of passengers waited in Asia and America. They all wanted to fly back to Europe, but the airports stayed closed for about one week. The ash cloud **5**_____ (finally / at first) went away. **6**_____ (When / While) the airports opened again, people started to fly home.

☐ TASK

3 ★★ Read the notes. Then complete the news item with information from the notes.

> Plane crash
> flight Brussels — Istanbul
> plane flies over Alps
> • 2 engines stop
>   pilots not worried — plane has 4 engines
> Milan airport — change direction
> • 3rd engine stops
>   plane slows down & loses height
>   pilots worried — fly over the mountains
> • 4th engine stops — fly over last mountain
>   crashes near a farm
>   rescue services help survivors all night
>   nobody is hurt
>   airline thanks pilots for their great work

Plane crash

There were dramatic scenes last night after the crash of a flight ___from Brussels to Istanbul___ . The plane was flying **1**_____. At first, the pilots **2**_____ because **3**_____. They spoke to Milan airport and **4**_____. Then **5**_____. As soon as this happened, the plane **6**_____ height. The pilots were worried because **7**_____. Finally, the fourth engine **8**_____ while **9**_____. Then the plane **10**_____ _____. **11**_____ and luckily, nobody died. After the crash, the airline **12**_____.

4 ★★★ Make notes about an interesting or important event that happened recently. Then write a news item.

MY EVALUATION   Check your progress. Do the exercises and then complete your own evaluation.

☐☐☐☐ I need to try this again.   ☐☐☐☐ I am happy with this.

☐☐☐☐ I could do this better.   ☐☐☐☐ I can do this very well.

VOCABULARY AND LANGUAGE FOCUS ●
Television

1 Complete the sentences with the words in the box.

> audience   channel   presenter
> character   programme   episodes

1 Was the show on a _____ with adverts?

2 It was amazing. There were 20,000 people in the _____.

3 The screen was tiny, so we couldn't read the _____'s name. I didn't know who was speaking.

4 It's better to watch that series on DVD. There are two extra _____.

5 I didn't enjoy this week's _____. It was really boring.

6 Which actor played the main _____ in that new drama series?

2 Complete the sentences using the correct forms of *was / were* and *there was / there were*.

Miki	[1]_____ Zac Efron on that chat show last night?
Sam97	Yes, but it [2]_____ very interesting, in my opinion.
Miki	Why not?
Sam97	I think Zac Efron is boring.
Miki	I don't agree with you. Zac Efron is great. [3]_____ any other guests on the show?
Sam97	I'm not sure. After that, we changed channels because [4]_____ some cool bands on BBC One.
Miki	Oh! What bands [5]_____ on BBC One?
Sam97	Lady Gaga and Usher. Usher [6]_____ amazing!
Miki	Wow! [7]_____ any other good programmes on TV last night?
Sam97	Yes, [8]_____ an interesting documentary, *Supersize Me*.

> **I can exchange opinions about TV.**
> MY EVALUATION   ☐☐☐☐

READING ● Reality TV

3 Complete the text. Use the past simple form of the verbs in brackets.

I [1]_____ (watch) an interesting reality show last night. It was about children who [2]_____ (have) problems with their behaviour. They [3]_____ (shout) all the time. Their parents were worried, so they [4]_____ (send) them on a special course.

As part of the course, the children [5]_____ (go) to a motorbike garage and they [6]_____ (learn) how to repair motorbikes. At first, they [7]_____ (complain) a lot, but by the end of the show, the children were really different. They were much happier and they [8]_____ (understand) how to control their feelings.

> **I can understand a text about reality TV.**
> MY EVALUATION   ☐☐☐☐

LANGUAGE FOCUS ● Past simple

4 Write the conversation. Use the past simple affirmative (✓), negative (✗), or question (?) form of the verbs.

Ann you / watch / *Tintin* yesterday ?
1 _____

Carl Yes, I did.
Ann where / you / see / it ?
2 _____

Carl I / go / to the Odeon with Marc ✓
3 _____

then we / have / lunch in a café ✓
4 _____

Ann you / call / me ✗
5 _____

Carl I / have / your number ✗
6 _____. Sorry.

> **I can talk about past events.**
> MY EVALUATION   ☐☐☐☐

VOCABULARY AND LISTENING ● On TV

5 Complete the text with the words in the box.

> documentary   medical drama   film
> reality show   sports programme

What's on TV?

- We meet the participants in *Feel the Fear*, the new ¹_____. In last week's show, the participants ate snakes and spiders. This week, they are swimming with sharks. Read more

- Dr Ali McAlastair, the main character in the ²_____ *Emergency*, left the show last night. How will Hornby Hospital survive? Read more

- In this new ³_____ series you can learn about the history of the United States from 1700 up to the 1970s. Read more

- James Cameron, the director of the 2010 hit *Avatar*, discusses his new ⁴_____. Read more

- Watch this week's top matches on ITV's new ⁵_____, *Football Special*. Read more

> **I can understand and present news.**
>
> MY EVALUATION ☐ ☐ ☐ ☐

LANGUAGE FOCUS ● Past tenses

6 Complete the sentences. Use the past simple and the past continuous form of the verbs in brackets.

1 You _____ (cry) when that sitcom _____ (finish)!
2 They _____ (go out) while their parents _____ (watch) the news.
3 The actors _____ (come) on stage while the presenter _____ (talk).
4 She _____ (not smile) when the man _____ (take) her photo.
5 Alice _____ (drop) her glass while she _____ (have) lunch.
6 It _____ (rain) when we _____ (arrive) at the cinema.

> **I can talk about what people were doing.**
>
> MY EVALUATION ☐ ☐ ☐ ☐

SPEAKING ● My news

7 Complete the conversation with the words in the box.

> about   fed up   happened   really   news

Erica Hi, Jared. You look ¹_____.
Jared Yes, I am. I've got some bad ²_____.
Erica ³_____? Tell me ⁴_____ it.
Jared Well, I bought the tickets for the James Bond film, but now I can't find them!
Erica Why not? What ⁵_____?
Jared I don't know. I'm so sorry.
Erica Hey, don't worry! My mum bought two tickets for us.

> **I can talk about my news.**
>
> MY EVALUATION ☐ ☐ ☐ ☐

WRITING ● A news article

8 Complete the news item with sentences a–f. There is one extra sentence that you do not need.

Crash closes road

¹_____ Police closed the A345 road in both directions for two hours after a car crash. ²_____ Mrs Aldate, 52, was driving along the A345 near Salisbury in Wiltshire when suddenly, a pig ran into the road. Mrs Aldate stopped her car very quickly. ³_____ Some people were walking on a hill near the road, when they heard the crash. ⁴_____ Then they saw a pig running away from the road and they noticed some smoke. They ran down to the road and they saw the crash. One of them called the emergency services. ⁵_____ Luckily, neither of the drivers was hurt.

a After a few minutes, an air ambulance arrived.
b At first, they didn't know what the noise was.
c There was a dramatic scene on a busy road in Wiltshire yesterday afternoon.
d Finally, the pig ran into the road.
e As soon as she stopped, another car crashed into the back of Mrs Aldate's car.
f The incident happened at 3.45 p.m.

> **I can write a news item.**
>
> MY EVALUATION ☐ ☐ ☐ ☐

VOCABULARY ● Household goods

1 ⭐ Match the words in the boxes.

a bottle of	toothpaste
a bar of	shampoo
a carton of	washing powder
a tube of	chocolate
a roll of	apples
a box of	juice
a bag of	fizzy drink
a can of	toilet paper

a bottle of shampoo

1 _____
2 _____
3 _____
4 _____
5 _____
6 _____
7 _____

2 ⭐⭐ Choose the correct answers.

Have you got a _____ of cola?

a bar   (**b** can)   **c** tube   **d** box

1 We're eating a big _____ of crisps.
   a carton   **b** bar   **c** can   **d** packet
2 I'd like a drink. Where's my _____ of water?
   a bar   **b** roll   **c** bottle   **d** box
3 She's got a _____ of oranges from the market.
   a bag   **b** tube   **c** can   **d** roll
4 Is there a _____ of coffee in the cupboard?
   a can   **b** jar   **c** bar   **d** tube
5 How many _____ of toilet paper does your family use each week?
   a jars   **b** bars   **c** bottles   **d** rolls
6 How much is that _____ of apple juice?
   a carton   **b** tube   **c** bag   **d** packet
7 We need to buy a _____ of soap at the supermarket.
   a roll   **b** bar   **c** can   **d** bottle
8 Can you buy a _____ of children's toothpaste for Emily?
   a jar   **b** bag   **c** tube   **d** packet

3 ⭐⭐ Complete the sentences with the words in the box.

| toothpaste   beans   ~~juice~~   toilet paper |
| washing powder   shampoo   chocolate |

Are you thirsty? Would you like this carton of _____*juice*____?

1 I want to wash my hair, but I can't find that bottle of _____.
2 Can we open the big bar of _____? We're hungry.
3 This can of _____ is very cheap.
4 Where's my tube of _____? I can't see it in the bathroom.
5 We need to buy some more rolls of _____. We haven't got any!
6 My T-shirt is very dirty. Have we got a new box of _____?

4 ⭐⭐⭐ Write sentences about the things that you have or haven't got at home.

In our fridge, *we've got two bottles of water, but we haven't got any cans of fizzy drink.*

1 In our fridge, _____
   _____.
2 In our kitchen cupboard, _____
   _____.
3 On our breakfast table, _____
   _____.
4 In our bathroom cupboard, _____
   _____.

much, many, a lot of, some, any

1 ★ Complete the table with *much, many, a lot of, some* or *any*.

much, many, a lot of	Countable	Uncountable
Affirmative	We eat a lot of potatoes.	We buy [1]_____ food.
Negative	I don't read many books.	I don't use [2]_____ milk.
Questions	How [3]_____ eggs do you eat?	How [4]_____ coffee do you drink?
some and any		
Affirmative	There are some bananas.	There's [5]_____ shampoo.
Negative	He hasn't got [6]_____ apples.	He hasn't got [7]_____ juice.
Questions	Are there [8]_____ oranges?	Is there [9]_____ tea?

2 ★★ Order the words to make sentences. There is one extra word that you do not need.

of / always / we / ~~many~~ / a / drink / coffee / lot
We always drink a lot of coffee.

1 isn't / there / milk / much / in / fridge / the / lot

_____.

2 much / fruit / eat / how / he / many / does / ?

_____.

3 aren't / some / there / eggs / the / any / box / in

_____.

4 hasn't / lot / many / CDs / got / hip hop / she

_____.

5 any / soap / some / there's / bathroom / the / in

_____.

6 much / your / has / brother / a / got / DVDs / of / lot

_____.

7 bag / apples / many / in / how / there / are / this / much / ?

_____.

Relative pronouns

3 ★★ Rewrite the sentences with *who, which* or *where*.

We visited a market. We bought some oranges.
We visited a market where we bought some oranges.

1 Yusuf read a blog. It was about the life of a family in New York.

_____
_____

2 Al Gore is an American. He made a famous film about the environment.

_____
_____

3 We went to Lily's house. I played with her dog.

_____
_____

4 His mother is a doctor. She works at the hospital in town.

_____
_____

5 I heard some music. It was really cool.

_____
_____

6 Cara went to a new shop. She met a friend.

_____
_____

4 ★★★ Complete the sentences using relative pronouns and your own ideas.

My mum is a person ___*who is very kind*___.

1 Football is a sport _____

2 Brad Pitt is an actor _____

3 Italy is the country _____

4 My best friend is a person _____

5 Coffee is a drink _____

6 New York is a place _____

7 English is a language _____

8 My town is a place _____

1 (★) Label the photos with the words in the box.

> pollute burn ~~destroy~~ throw away
> bury recycle

___destroy___   1 _____

2 _____   3 _____

4 _____   5 _____

2 (★★) Match verbs 1–6 with sentences from newspapers a–f.

1 throw away ___b___   4 recycle _____
2 destroy _____   5 bury _____
3 poison _____   6 burn _____

a 'Don't put rubbish in the ground!' says the environmental group.

b Did you know … ? Americans put 25 billion plastic bottles in their bins every year.

c The worst forest fires in Australia since 1983!

d Last year, people cut down more than 15,000 km² of the Amazon rainforest.

e Local council wants people to reuse more bottles.

f Disaster! Water pollution is killing fish.

3 (★★) Complete the sentences with the words in the box.

> poison pollutes destroy waste
> burn save reuse ~~recycle~~

It's important to ___recycle___ more paper and glass.

1 Some families buy a lot of food and don't eat it. They _____ it.

2 Rubbish in the river can _____ the fish.

3 People must _____ the tigers in India.

4 It's bad for the environment to _____ plastic bags.

5 We sometimes _____ plastic cartons. We put small plants in them.

6 Using cars _____ the atmosphere.

7 It's wrong to _____ trees. We need them!

4 (★★★) Complete the text using verbs in exercises 2 and 3.

WHAT CAN YOU DO TO SAVE THE PLANET?

Don't ___throw away___ your old clothes and put them in the bin. You can ¹_____ them. Take them to the special recycling centre in Church Road.

Also, you can write to your local council. Ask them not to ²_____ rubbish because the smoke ³_____ the atmosphere.

It isn't a good idea to ⁴_____ plastic bags in the ground either.

When you get a plastic bag, don't forget to ⁵_____ it several times.

Make sure that you eat all the food in your fridge – don't throw it in the bin and ⁶_____ it!

1 ★ Complete the table with *too, too much, too many* or *enough*.

With adjectives	With countable nouns	With uncountable nouns
The bag is ___too___ small.	There are [1]_____ _____ bottles.	There's [2]_____ _____ pollution.
Is it big enough?	Are there [3]_____ books?	Is there [4]_____ water?
It isn't strong [5]_____.	There aren't enough chairs.	There isn't [6]_____ food.

2 ★★ Complete the sentences with *too, too much, too many* or *enough*.

He's _____too_____ tired to walk home.

1 Our dog is very fat. I think we give him _____ food every day.
2 I can't do my geography homework. It's _____ difficult!
3 I can't go to the cinema. I've only got £2 and that isn't _____.
4 We use _____ plastic bags!
5 Is your brother old _____ to go on holiday without your parents?
6 There's _____ rubbish on our streets.

3 ★★ Write new sentences with *too* or *not enough*.

My shopping bag is too small.

~~My shopping bag isn't big enough.~~ _____ (big)

1 Our oceans aren't clean enough.
_____ (dirty)
2 Those concert tickets aren't cheap enough.
_____ (expensive)
3 The swimming pool is too far.
_____ (near)
4 Her brother is too young for that disco.
_____ (old)
5 That laptop is too heavy.
_____ (light)
6 Your old bike isn't safe enough.
_____ (dangerous)

4 ★★ Complete the dialogues with *too much* or *too many* and the words in the box.

~~players~~   books   CDs   noise   cars
visitors   homework

Can I join your football team? → No, we've got ___too many players___.

1 I can't hear you! → Sorry! There's _____ _____ in here!
2 Why is this box so heavy? → Oh dear, I think I put ____ _____ in it.
3 It's impossible to drive in our town. → Yes, I think there are _____.
4 Are you going to buy that CD? → No, I've got _____ _____ at home.
5 Would you like to come to the cinema? → Sorry, I've got _____ _____ this evening.
6 The zoo is really busy today. → Yes, there are _____ _____ here.

5 ★★★ Write sentences about your town with some of the words in the box. Use *too, too much, too many, enough* or *not enough*.

~~cars~~   motorbikes   buses   cinemas   wet
discos   noise   traffic   rubbish   boring
entertainment   rain   sun   hot   old   dirty

There are too many cars in the centre of town.

1 _____
_____
2 _____
_____
3 _____
_____
4 _____
_____
5 _____
_____

1 ★ Read the text. Tick ✓ the correct box.

The text is about designers who ...

a ☐ save energy at their fashion shows.
b ☐ never throw away clothes.
c ☐ make clothes from recycled materials.

Recycled style

A People from all over the world come to London Fashion Week. This year, one fashion show at the Science Museum is different. Models walk down the catwalk to loud music and photographers take hundreds of pictures. But that happens in every show, so what's different? The answer is, of course, the clothes.

B All the models are wearing clothes made from reused materials which usually end up in our rubbish bins. For example, one model is wearing a hat and jewellery made from old CDs, another is wearing a jacket made from firemen's old trousers and another is wearing a pair of shoes created from car seats.

C The show is from five 'eco–designers' who all have new collections. They want to make clothes, but not create waste. These designers recycle and reuse old materials to create their new styles.

D The designers are all worried about the impact of clothes on the environment. 'We are seeing a culture where people are buying clothes, then throwing them away,' says one of the designers. 'We need to recycle much more.'

E Every year in the UK, people throw away two billion kilograms of clothes, which often come from cheap fashion shops. This creates too much rubbish for councils and it's sometimes difficult to recycle the materials.

2 ★★ Match topics 1–5 with paragraphs A–E.

1 The problem of cheap clothes ___E___
2 Designers who recycle _____
3 Clothes made from rubbish _____
4 One designer's opinion _____
5 A fashion show with a difference _____

3 ★★ Read the text again. Write *true* or *false*.

Only people from the UK come to London Fashion Week.   _false_

1 Photographers take a lot of pictures at the show. _____
2 All the models wear firemen's trousers. _____
3 A designer made jewellery from old CDs. _____
4 The show has clothes from two designers. _____
5 People often recycle clothes from cheap fashion shops. _____
6 Recycling materials can sometimes be a problem. _____

4 ★★★ Answer the questions. Write complete sentences.

Where is the fashion show?
<u>It's at the Science Museum in London.</u>

1 What did one of the designers use to make a jacket?
_____

2 What did one of the designers use car seats for?
_____

3 What are these special designers called?
_____

4 What worries the designers?
_____

5 What does one designer think we need to do?
_____

6 Why is it a problem that people throw away a lot of clothes?
_____

Build your vocabulary

5 ★★ Complete the sentences with the words in the box.

> ~~centre~~   ice cream   sandwich   present
> paper   powder

Let's go to the shopping __centre__.

1 I'd like a cheese _____.
2 Use this washing _____!
3 My bag was a birthday _____.
4 Clean the table with this kitchen _____!
5 Would you like a strawberry _____?

Language point: *so* and *because*

1 ⭐ **Choose the correct words.**

The beach is dirty **so** / (**because**) everybody leaves rubbish on it.

1 It's bad to bury plastic **so** / **because** it doesn't decompose.
2 He was unhappy about the problem, **so** / **because** he wrote a letter to the council.
3 I've got a shopping bag, **so** / **because** I don't need to use plastic bags.
4 We're worried about plastic bags **so** / **because** they're bad for the environment.
5 I feel cheerful today **so** / **because** it's my birthday.
6 They were very hungry, **so** / **because** they ate a packet of biscuits.

2 ⭐⭐ **Match sentence halves 1–6 with a–f.**

1 Marc was very hungry,
2 Tim was feeling ill
3 Laura broke her leg,
4 My mum came home late
5 They were very tired
6 They wanted to catch the first train,

a so they got up early.
b so she went to hospital.
c because he ate too much chocolate.
d so he ate three packets of crisps.
e because she spent an hour at the doctor's.
f because they always went to bed late.

☐ TASK

3 ⭐⭐ **Read the notes and complete Ben's letter to the council.**

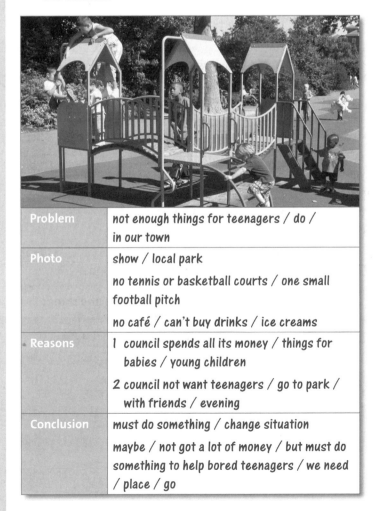

Problem	not enough things for teenagers / do / in our town
Photo	show / local park
	no tennis or basketball courts / one small football pitch
	no café / can't buy drinks / ice creams
Reasons	1 council spends all its money / things for babies / young children
	2 council not want teenagers / go to park / with friends / evening
Conclusion	must do something / change situation
	maybe / not got a lot of money / but must do something to help bored teenagers / we need / place / go

Dear Sir or Madam,

I'm writing because there **aren't enough things for teenagers to do** in our town. I'm sending you a photo which ¹_____. There are no ²_____ and there's only ³_____. Also, there isn't a ⁴_____.

I think there are possibly two reasons for for this problem. Firstly, the council ⁵_____.

Secondly, the council doesn't want ⁶_____.

We must ⁷_____. Maybe the council ⁸_____, but we ⁹_____.

Yours faithfully,

Ben Wolf

4 ⭐⭐⭐ **Write a letter to your council. Imagine there isn't enough for teenagers to do where you live. Describe the causes of the problems and suggest solutions.**

MY EVALUATION   Check your progress. Do the exercises and then complete your own evaluation.

☐☐☐☐ I need to try this again.   ☐☐☐☐ I am happy with this.

☐☐☐☐ I could do this better.   ☐☐☐☐ I can do this very well.

VOCABULARY AND LANGUAGE FOCUS ●
Household goods

1 Complete the dialogues with the words in the box.

> can   bar   carton   roll   tube   bag

1 Do you eat a lot of sweets?
Not really. I have a small _____ of chocolate every week.

2 How many things did you get in the shop?
We only bought a _____ of toothpaste!

3 You don't drink much water with your food.
But I always have a _____ of fizzy drink.

4 Do you want any fruit today?
Yes, I'd like a _____ of apples, please.

5 We need to do some shopping.
Yes, I mustn't forget to get a _____ of toilet paper.

6 Are you thirsty?
Yes. Can I have a _____ of orange juice, please?

2 Choose the correct words.

1 How **much / many** plastic bags do you use?
2 There are **a lot of / many** bottles to recycle.
3 We've got **some / many** potatoes in the cupboard, but we need more for dinner.
4 How **many / much** water does your dog drink every day?
5 My sister hasn't got **some / any** money. She spent it all last week.
6 How **many / much** fuel does your car use?

> **I can talk about quantities of things people use.**
>
> MY EVALUATION ☐☐☐☐

READING ● The 'no impact' family

3 Match sentence halves 1–6 with a–f.

1	They use recycled kitchen	a	powder.
2	They don't use much washing	b	sandwiches.
3	They don't give Christmas	c	paper.
4	They make their own strawberry	d	centre.
5	They don't eat chicken	e	presents.
6	They don't go to the shopping	f	ice cream.

> **I can understand a text about a 'no impact' family.**
>
> MY EVALUATION ☐☐☐☐

LANGUAGE FOCUS ● Relative pronouns

4 Complete the sentences with *who, which* or *where*.

1 A zoo is a place _____ you can see wild animals.
2 Cristiano Ronaldo is a famous footballer _____ plays for Portugal.
3 The Siberian tiger is an animal _____ can run very fast.
4 Miley Cyrus is an actress and singer _____ comes from the USA.
5 Cappuccino is a drink _____ you make with coffee and milk.
6 A supermarket is a shop _____ people can buy different types of food.

> **I can talk about places, people and things using relative pronouns.**
>
> MY EVALUATION ☐☐☐☐

VOCABULARY AND LISTENING ● Pollution and the environment

5 Complete the words in the sentences.

1 Do you re _ _ _ any of your plastic cartons?
2 People mustn't de _ _ _ _ _ the rainforest.
3 If the council puts dirty water in the sea, it can po _ _ _ _ the fish.
4 I never th _ _ _ _ _ _ _ my old clothes. I always re _ _ _ _ _ them.
5 'Is it wrong to bu _ _ plastic?'
  'Yes, it can po _ _ _ _ _ the atmosphere.'
6 We must sa _ _ the elephants in Africa.
7 They buy food, but then they wa _ _ _ it.
8 It's bad to bu _ _ rubbish under the ground.

> **I can understand a programme about the problems with plastic bags.**
>
> MY EVALUATION ☐☐☐☐

LANGUAGE FOCUS ● *too, too much, too many, enough, not enough*

6 Complete the sentences with one of the expressions in brackets.

1 I don't usually drink coffee. It's _____ strong for me. (too / too much / enough)
2 Have you got _____ money to buy a drink? (too much / too many / enough)
3 You mustn't eat _____ sweets. They're bad for you. (enough / too / too many)
4 Don't buy that packet of crisps. It isn't big _____ for all of us. (too much / enough / too)
5 It's terrible! People waste _____ food. (too many / too much / enough)
6 We can never eat those pizzas. They're _____ big. (too many / too much / too)

> **I can talk about eating habits.**
>
> MY EVALUATION ☐☐☐☐

SPEAKING ● Offering and asking for help

7 Put the dialogue in the correct order. Number the sentences.

a ☐ Olivia OK, no problem. Bye!
b ☐ Olivia No, that's fine. I know a good shop which sells drinks.
c ☐ Olivia Hi, Harry! Have we got everything for the party?
d ☐ Olivia Do you want me to buy some more drinks?
e ☐ Harry Thanks. That would be great. Could you get five cartons of juice and ten cans of fizzy drink?
f ☐ Harry Well, we've got enough food, but there isn't much to drink.
g ☐ Harry Do you mind?

> **I can offer and ask for help.**
>
> MY EVALUATION ☐☐☐☐

WRITING ● An environmental problem

8 Complete the text with the words in the box.

> secondly   shows   so   firstly   about
> possibly   because   for

We're writing ¹_____ we were in the park yesterday and we found a lot of rubbish there. This photo ²_____ the old cartons, jars and packets which we found.

We think there are ³_____ two reasons ⁴_____ all the rubbish. ⁵_____, there aren't enough bins and a lot of people aren't careful enough, ⁶_____ they leave their old cans and plastic bags everywhere.

⁷_____, nobody looks after the park or takes away all the rubbish. We need somebody to clean the place every day.

The rubbish in our park is a real problem. We must do something ⁸_____ it.

Lydia Field and Abigail Proctor

> **I can write about an environmental problem.**
>
> MY EVALUATION ☐☐☐☐

3 ⬛⬜⬜⬜⬜⬜⬜⬜⬜⬜ Life online

VOCABULARY ▪ The internet

1 (★) **Complete the internet-related nouns.**

d _ownload_

1 instant m_____
2 p_____ webpage
3 file s_____
4 m_____ board
5 email a_____
6 o_____ game
7 search e_____

2 (★★) **Do the *Computer Quiz*.**

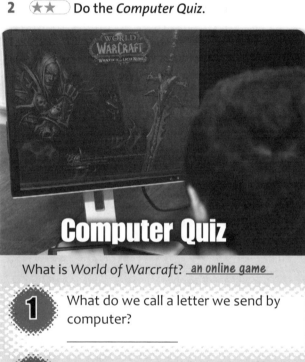

Computer Quiz

What is *World of Warcraft*? _an online game_

1 What do we call a letter we send by computer?
_____

2 Where can you speak to your friends online?
_____

3 Where can you leave online notes for your friends?
_____

4 What helps you to look for information online?
_____

5 What is like an online diary?
_____

6 What can you use to see your friends while you are chatting?
_____

3 (★★) **Complete the sentences with the words in the box.**

> blog   create   download   email   ~~play~~
> post   search   send   use

We ___play___ games online every day.

1 I _____ my friends all the time.
2 Did he _____ his personal webpage?
3 Let's _____ a message about this game.
4 I can _____ it as an email attachment.
5 When do you _____ your webcam?
6 Let's _____ for that information on *Wikipedia*.
7 I _____ every day. I've written 276 pages!
8 I forgot to _____ the new version of this game.

4 (★★★) **Answer the questions. Write complete sentences.**

Do you play games online? What online games do you play?
I play FarmVille with my cousin.

1 Do you prefer calling friends on your mobile, texting, or chatting online? Why?
_____
_____

2 What type of things do you download?
_____
_____

3 What type of things do you usually search for online?
_____
_____

4 Do you email people often? Who do you email?
_____

5 Do you know anybody who's got a personal webpage? Who?
_____
_____

6 Have you got a webcam? When do you use it?
_____
_____

Present perfect: affirmative and negative

1 ★ Complete the table with *has, hasn't, have* or *haven't*.

Affirmative		
I / You	__have__	emailed a photo.
He / She / It	¹_____	appeared on *YouTube*.
We / You / They	²_____	shared files.
Negative		
I / You	³_____	created a webpage.
He / She / It	⁴_____	played an online game.
We / You / They	⁵_____	used a webcam.

2 ★★ Write sentences using the present perfect.

we / download / the new Dizzee Rascal album
We've downloaded the new Dizzee Rascal album.

1 Tom / not create / a personal webpage
_____
_____

2 I / play / some new online games
_____
_____

3 she / join / an online chess club
_____
_____

4 fifty people / log on / to our website
_____
_____

5 I / not message / my friends today
_____
_____

6 your grandma / not use / a computer
_____
_____

7 they / not chat / online before
_____
_____

8 we / visit / your website
_____
_____

Present perfect: regular and irregular verbs

3 ★★ Mrs Foster's class is creating a webpage. Read Mike's notes. What have or haven't the students done? Write sentences.

Year 11 website
Mike > buy the web address ✓
1 Mike and Jacob > design the website ✗
2 Rob > take photos for the site ✓
3 Bev and Harry > interview
   Year 13 students ✓
4 Bev and Harry > write the stories ✗
5 Year 11 > put the information online ✗
6 Mrs Foster > tell the other classes about
   the website ✗

Mike has bought the web address.
1 _____
2 _____
3 _____
4 _____
5 _____
6 _____

4 ★★★ Write sentences about you, your family and your friends. Use the phrases in the box and the present perfect.

create a personal webpage
play games online   email friends
use a search engine   blog   share files

My friends and I have created a personal webpage.
1 _____
   _____
2 _____
   _____
3 _____
   _____
4 _____
   _____
5 _____
   _____
6 _____
   _____

1 ⭐ Find seven more words.

E	P	A	S	S	W	O	R	D	T
M	H	E	P	S	O	D	E	N	I
A	I	H	A	C	K	E	R	Z	N
L	S	O	M	E	S	S	A	V	B
L	H	F	F	I	E	T	N	I	O
S	I	D	I	M	M	O	E	R	X
N	N	I	L	O	S	S	D	U	N
O	G	P	T	P	P	L	E	S	E
F	I	R	E	W	A	L	L	E	D
T	S	E	R	O	M	M	E	D	Y

___spam filter___

1 _____   5 _____
2 _____   6 _____
3 _____   7 _____
4 _____

2 ⭐⭐ Choose the correct answers.

The bank lost £1 million after a _____ attack.

(a phishing)   b password   c spam filter

1 I always get lots of _____.
   a inbox   b spam   c password
2 The _____ has damaged millions of computers.
   a inbox   b password   c virus
3 The _____ didn't protect my computer from the virus.
   a hacker   b anti-virus software
   c spam
4 Have you installed a new _____?
   a hacker   b spam filter   c phishing
5 I hate _____! Who sends it?
   a junk mail   b firewall   c inbox
6 This new _____ will protect your computer.
   a spam   b firewall   c phishing
7 Don't tell anyone your _____.
   a hacker   b spam filter   c password

3 ⭐⭐ Complete the text with the words in the box.

> ~~anti-virus software~~   firewalls   hackers
> passwords   phishing   spam   viruses

ComputerExpert.com   >Bookmark this site

| Home | Support | Products | Forum |

Simple ways to protect yourself

- Every computer connected to the internet needs security. You can install __anti-virus software__ to protect your computer from ¹_____. Use different ²_____ when you log on to different sites.

- We recommend one of our safe ³_____ to stop ⁴_____. Nobody can get past them!

Dealing with junk email

- Cybercriminals send millions of junk emails because they want you to answer with your personal details. This is called ⁵_____. Remember! Most web crime happens through email; never open ⁶_____, especially if it has attachments.

4 ⭐⭐⭐ Answer the questions. Write complete sentences.

How many passwords have you got?
I've got three, one for my computer, one for Facebook, and one for my email.

1 Do you use any security for your PC? What kind?
   _____
   _____

2 How many spam emails do you get a week?
   _____

3 Have you ever opened and read spam? If yes, what did it say?
   _____
   _____

4 Do you shop online? What do you buy?
   _____

5 Do you think shopping online is safe? Why / Why not?
   _____
   _____

3

1 (★) Complete the questions with *have* or *has*.

_____Have_____ you ever blogged?

1 _____ she ever chatted online?
2 _____ they ever shared files?
3 _____ Jack read this message board?
4 What _____ you emailed?
5 Why _____ she downloaded that file?
6 Where _____ we posted a message?

2 (★★) Complete the questions in the survey using the present perfect form of the verbs in brackets. Then answer the questions.

Downham Secondary School

IT SKILLS SURVEY

Which internet search engines _____have_____ you _____used_____ (use)?

	YES / NO
1 _____ you ever _____ (download) files from the internet?	☐ ☐
2 _____ you ever _____ (email) an attachment?	☐ ☐
3 _____ you ever _____ (use) an Apple Mac?	☐ ☐
4 _____ your friends ever _____ (create) a personal webpage?	☐ ☐
5 _____ you ever _____ (install) a software program?	☐ ☐
6 _____ your class _____ (learn) to use Word?	☐ ☐
7 Which other software programs _____ your class _____ (study)?	

---

3 (★★) Write questions using the present perfect.

what / Charlie / make
What has Charlie made?

1 they / see / our website
_____

2 why / you / give / me this password
_____
_____

3 which / blogs / he / read
_____

4 they / email / the attachments
_____

5 Clare / create / a new webpage
_____

6 where / he / post / the messages
_____
_____

7 you / receive / spam
_____

8 who / send / me this email
_____

4 (★★★) Read the answers. Then write the questions. Use the present perfect form of the verbs in bold.

Have you visited John's website?

Yes, I have. I **visited** John's website this morning.

1 _____
_____?
No, I haven't. I've never **played** Super Mario.

2 _____?
No, he hasn't. He's never **created** a new webpage.

3 Where _____?
I'm not sure. Maybe they've **gone** to the library.

4 _____?
Yes, they have **downloaded** the film.

5 What _____?
She's **sent** a few photos.

6 _____
_____?
No, I haven't. I've never **shared** files.

1 ⭐ Read the text. Tick ✓ the correct box.

The writer wrote this text to …

a ☐ give information about a website.
b ☐ ask for advice.
c ☐ improve his / her English.

Teen Second Life

Jan Hofman has never scored less than 80% in an English test and his spoken English is amazing. But Jan hasn't had extra English classes at school and he hasn't read an English dictionary. In fact, Jan spends at least three hours a day playing a game online. What's his secret? Why is Jan so brilliant at English? His secret is TSL – Teen Second Life.

TSL is a virtual world for thirteen to seventeen-year-olds and it's free to join. In TSL, teenagers from around the world have their own avatar. Avatars can go shopping and spend money – 'Linden dollars' – in the shops. They can make friends and play sports. They can even join a band and play music!

How has TSL helped Jan Hofman to improve his English? 'There are a lot of places in TSL where you can improve your English,' explains Jan. 'The British Council has got a special island in TSL and I've spent most of my time there. They don't give English lessons, but there are games and competitions in English. I also like the Global Kids island, where I learn a lot about social and world problems, all in English. The best thing about TSL is simply chatting. I love messaging players from other countries. I think anyone who wants to practise their English should log on to TSL!'

2 ⭐⭐ Find the words in the text and match them with the definitions.

1 score ⎯⎯⎯ a very good
2 brilliant ⎯⎯ b about society
3 social c to get better at something
4 avatar ⎯⎯ d to get points
5 improve e online character

3 ⭐⭐ Read the text again. Choose the correct answers.

Jan Hofman's English is _____.
(a very good) b OK c really bad

1 Jan Hofman _____.
a reads dictionaries
b has extra English classes
c plays a game online

2 TSL is _____.
a a school b a dictionary c a game

3 TSL has helped Jan to _____.
a practise English b learn about England
c spend money

4 Jan enters competitions on the _____ island.
a British Council's b Global Kids c Linden

5 TSL is a good place to _____.
a play computer games
b communicate in English
c discuss the world's problems

4 ⭐⭐⭐ Answer the questions. Write complete sentences.

Does Jan spend a long time online?
Yes, he spends at least three hours a day online.

1 How much does it cost to join TSL?
_____

2 Who can join TSL?
_____

3 What can avatars do in TSL?
_____

4 What does Jan do on the Global Kids island?
_____

5 What has Jan enjoyed most about TSL?
_____

6 Who does Jan chat with?
_____

Build your vocabulary

5 ⭐⭐ Match sentence halves 1–6 with a–f.

1 I turn on the ⎯⎯ a the girl in the photo.
2 He felt very b my money on my new laptop.
3 They made a lot of c computer when I get home.
4 She recognized d battles in the online game.
5 I spent all of e sad when his cat died.
6 They fought f noise at the party.

Language point: Addition and contrast linkers

1 ⭐ Choose the correct words.

I (**also**) / **too** like instant messaging.

1 **Although** / **However** I always email people, I've never sent an attachment.
2 He blogs, **but** / **too** he's never created a website.
3 We've played games online and we've chatted **too** / **although**.
4 He messages me all the time. **Also** / **However**, he isn't online right now.
5 I've posted a message and I've **although** / **also** emailed her.
6 We've logged on to TSL, **but** / **also** we haven't played it.

2 ⭐⭐ Complete the sentences with the words in the box.

> also ~~although~~ although but
> however too but

___Although___ he downloaded anti-virus software, his computer had a virus.

1 My laptop was expensive, _____ it wasn't as expensive as your computer.
2 I've played games with my cousin, and my uncle, _____.
3 I've installed a firewall to protect my computer. _____, it doesn't always work.
4 We've chatted and we've _____ used a webcam.
5 _____ I've created the webpage, I haven't sent him the password.
6 I've played chess online, _____ I haven't won any games.

○ TASK

3 ⭐⭐ Read the notes about people's opinions. Then complete the comments.

James007
not download music
people download music / not pay for it = problem
bands need money / work hard
illegal downloading = stealing

PopLife444
record companies = enough money
not download music illegally
share CDs / friends
buy a song > friends enjoy
not a problem (= lend books)

Are illegal downloads killing music?

Post a comment   Report to moderator

James007
I've **never downloaded music**. However, I know people who download music and they
¹_____. Some people say it doesn't matter, but I think that ²_____.
Bands need money, and ³_____, too. Have you ever gone into a food shop, for example, and walked out without paying? ⁴_____ stealing, too!

PopLife444
I disagree with James007. Record companies
⁵_____. I've never
⁶_____. However, I
⁷_____. When I buy music, why can't my ⁸_____? I don't think
⁹_____. It's the same as lending books.

4 ⭐⭐⭐ Do you agree or disagree with the opinion below? Write your own opinion comment for a website. Use some addition and contrast linkers.

Chatting online is better than talking on the phone.

MY EVALUATION   Check your progress. Do the exercises and then complete your own evaluation.

☐☐☐☐ I need to try this again.   ☐☐☐☐ I am happy with this.

☐☐☐☐ I could do this better.   ☐☐☐☐ I can do this very well.

VOCABULARY AND LANGUAGE FOCUS ●
The internet

1 Complete the sentences with the words in the box.

> shared   online games   message   post
> messaging   webcam   webpage

1 Who created your personal _____?
2 Have you ever _____ files?
3 I never play _____.
4 My mum has never used a _____.
5 I _____ people all the time.
6 I love instant _____.
7 Where do you _____ messages?

2 Write affirmative or negative present perfect sentences about your own internet experiences.

1 I _____.
(message people)

2 I _____.
(share files)

3 I _____
_____.
(post messages)

4 I _____
_____.
(create a personal webpage)

5 I _____
_____.
(play games online)

6 I _____
_____.
(use a webcam)

7 I _____.
(blog)

8 I _____
_____.
(chat with somebody from another country)

> **I can talk about my experiences.**
>
> MY EVALUATION ☐☐☐☐

READING ● Internet addiction

3 Complete the text with the words in the box.

> makes   feels   fights   play
> recognize   spends   turns on

My cousin the internet addict

My cousin is an internet addict. He [1]_____ about 15 hours online every day. His family are worried. He has changed a lot lately. They don't [2]_____ him. He doesn't eat. His mum [3]_____ him sandwiches, but he leaves them. We invite him to interesting places, but he only wants to [4]_____ games online.

He has never joined Facebook and he doesn't send emails. He just [5]_____ his computer every afternoon and he [6]_____ battles until late at night. He never talks and I think he [7]_____ angry and depressed, but he doesn't think that's he's an addict. It's sad.

> **I can understand a text about internet addiction.**
>
> MY EVALUATION ☐☐☐☐

LANGUAGE FOCUS ● Present perfect: regular and irregular verbs

4 Complete the sentences so that they are true for you. Use the affirmative or negative present perfect form of the verbs in brackets.

1 I _____ (be) online all day.
2 My best friend _____ (spend) a lot of time online today.
3 I _____ (search) the internet this week.
4 My mum / dad _____ (email) me.
5 My best friend and I _____ (chat) online this month.
6 I _____ (send) email attachments.

> **I can talk about internet use.**
>
> MY EVALUATION ☐☐☐☐

VOCABULARY AND LISTENING ● Cybercrime

5 Choose the correct answers and complete the programme information.

Cybercriminals and YOU

20:45–21:35   BBC3

In this week's programme, learn about the three main ways that cybercriminals can attack your computer:

Hacking

Hackers can get past your ¹_____ and steal information, often using your password.

Phishing

Sometimes your ²_____ doesn't stop junk emails, and some of this spam can be ³_____ emails.

Viruses

Good anti-virus ⁴_____ is important because viruses can hide in email attachments. When you click and open the attachment, the ⁵_____ attacks your hard drive and your problems begin.

1 **a** spam	**b** firewall	**c** inbox
2 **a** hacker	**b** spam filter	**c** password
3 **a** software	**b** firewall	**c** phishing
4 **a** password	**b** phishing	**c** software
5 **a** virus	**b** spam	**c** firewall

> **I can talk about cybercrime.**
>
> MY EVALUATION ☐☐☐☐

LANGUAGE FOCUS ● Present perfect: questions

6 Write present perfect questions.

1 you / ever / create / a personal webpage?

_____

2 you / ever / use / a webcam?

_____

3 what songs / you / download / this month?

_____

4 who / you / email / recently?

_____

5 which websites / you / visit / today?

_____

> **I can ask and answer about experiences.**
>
> MY EVALUATION ☐☐☐☐

SPEAKING ● Apologizing and explaining

7 Complete the dialogue with the words in the box.

> happen   matter   mean   relief
> sorry   what

Tia   I've got something to tell you.

Mum   ¹_____ is it? What's the ²_____?

Tia   I've done something really stupid.

Mum   What have you done?

Tia   It's your mp3 player. I've broken it. I'm really ³_____! I was listening to it and it fell on the floor.

Mum   How did that happen?

Tia   I don't know. I didn't ⁴_____ to.

Mum   It's OK. My music's on my laptop, too.

Tia   That's a ⁵_____! It won't ⁶_____ again. I promise!

> **I can apologize for something and explain how it happened.**
>
> MY EVALUATION ☐☐☐☐

WRITING ● A comment on a website

8 Complete the text.

> My best friend thinks that everybody needs a smartphone. However, ¹_____ my opinion, normal mobile phones are fine. In ²_____ experience, most people only need a phone to text and make calls. ³_____ what I've seen, Facebook is the only website people visit with their smartphones. The ⁴_____ is that the smartphone screen is too small, so you can't really read most websites. ⁵_____ this reason, I ⁶_____ normal mobile phones are better.

> **I can write an opinion comment on a website.**
>
> MY EVALUATION ☐☐☐☐

VOCABULARY ● Adjectives: personality

1 ⭐ **Complete the crossword.**

```
      ¹C U R I O U ²S
   ³G
⁴S  ⁵M                        ⁶I
    ⁷S            ⁸S
⁹I
          ¹⁰I
             ¹¹F
```

Across

1 He asks a lot of questions in class.
  He's very ___curious___.
5 They never spend money.
  They're _____.
7 She didn't laugh at the film.
  She's very _____.
9 You never listen to other people's ideas.
  You're really _____.
10 He did well in the test.
  He's _____.
11 She always talks to me.
  She's _____.

Down

1 I'm going to pass the exam.
  I feel _____ about it.
2 We didn't enjoy the party.
  We're a bit _____.
3 You often give me presents.
  You're very _____.
4 She always gives good practical advice. She's
  very _____.
6 Megan is three. She doesn't know much
  about the world. She's _____.
8 We cried when we watched that sad film.
  We're really _____.

2 ⭐⭐ **Choose the correct answers.**

He wants to be a film star. He's very _____.
  a generous (**b** ambitious) **c** mean
1 Our sister plays basketball, tennis and
  football. She's very _____.
  a innocent **b** intelligent **c** active
2 My dad can repair bikes because he's _____.
  a innocent **b** intolerant **c** practical
3 You must be more _____ and try to
  understand other people.
  a tolerant **b** active **c** mean
4 I'm a very _____ person. I get what I want!
  a generous **b** determined **c** friendly
5 Don't be _____! Come and talk to us!
  a shy **b** sensible **c** sensitive
6 You aren't very _____. What's happened?
  a mean **b** cheerful **c** curious

3 ⭐⭐⭐ **Complete the text with words in
exercises 1 and 2.**

Actor Daniel Radcliffe
is famous because he
played Harry Potter,
but what is Daniel
really like and what
do we know about his
personality?

  Daniel smiles a lot
and he's a ___cheerful___
person. He's ¹_____
to his fans and he often says
'hello' to them.

  The actor is very rich, but he doesn't buy a
lot of expensive things, he's always very
²_____ with his money. He isn't a mean
person – he's ³_____ and he sometimes
gives money to help charities.

  We know that he's ⁴_____ because he
did very well in his exams at school. He wants to
learn new things so he's a ⁵_____ person,
too. He also reads a lot of books and he can be
very quiet and ⁶_____.

LANGUAGE FOCUS ◼ Adverbs of degree • Present perfect + *still*, *yet*, *just* and *already*

Adverbs of degree

1 ★ Complete the words in the table.

******	It's <u>i n c r e d i b l y</u> easy. Everybody can do it.
*****	I'm ¹<u>r _ a _ l _</u> hungry. I want to eat dinner now!
****	He's ²<u>v _ r _</u> practical. He can make things.
***	The film was ³<u>q _ i _ e</u> good, but I preferred the last one.
**	You're a ⁴<u>b _ t</u> late. I arrived five minutes ago.
*	She isn't ⁵<u>v _ _ y</u> friendly. She doesn't talk to me.

2 ★★ Rewrite the sentences with adverbs of degree.

My older sister is confident. *****
<u>My older sister is really confident.</u>

1 I'm tolerant at home.*
_____

2 This football match is exciting.****
_____

3 That young artist is ambitious. ******
_____

4 Some teenagers go to bed late. ***
_____

5 That exam question is difficult. **
_____

Present perfect + *still*, *yet*, *just* and *already*

3 ★★ Write sentences using the present perfect and the word in brackets.

we / listen to / that CD (already)
<u>We've already listened to that CD.</u>

1 I / watch / this film (already)
_____

2 he / play / a new song (just)
_____

3 Daniel / become / a celebrity / ? (yet)
_____

4 we / not finish / our new album (still)
_____

5 they / start / their tour / ? (yet)
_____

4 ★★ Complete the sentences. Use the present perfect with *just* and the words in the box.

> come out of the sea   ~~go out~~   have lunch
> ask the teacher   have an accident
> play tennis   win a competition

My brother isn't at home. He <u>'s just gone out</u>.

1 They aren't very hungry. They _____
_____.

2 You know the answer. You _____
_____.

3 I've got a prize. I _____.
4 The dog is wet. It _____.
5 We've got our rackets with us. We _____
_____.

6 She's in the hospital. She _____
_____.

5 ★★★ Write sentences with *still*, *yet* or *already*. Use the words in the box and your own ideas.

> **visit:** my local art gallery
> my local museum
> the capital of my country
> the biggest stadium in my country

> **try:** Chinese food   French food
> Mexican food   Indian food

> **learn to:** make pizza
> make a good cup of coffee
> iron my clothes
> use the washing machine

I still haven't visited <u>my local art gallery</u>.

1 _____
2 _____
3 _____
4 _____
5 _____
6 _____
7 _____
8 _____

VOCABULARY ● Nouns and adjectives: personal qualities

1 ⭐ **Choose the correct words.**

You need (skill) / skilful to be a professional footballer.

1 Nicole Kidman has got a lot of **style / stylish**.
2 The actor in the film is very **good looks / good-looking**.
3 Some people think that you don't need much **talent / talented** to be a model.
4 When you leave school, you need to be more **independence / independent**.
5 Wrestlers are always very **strength / strong**.
6 An astronaut needs to be very **courage / courageous**.
7 That singer is difficult to work with. He's got a very big **ego / egotistical**.
8 You usually need a lot of **luck / lucky** to become a film star.

2 ⭐⭐ **Complete the text with the correct nouns and adjectives.**

Penélope Cruz is a t _alented_____ actress who was born in Alcobendas, Madrid, in 1974. She's
¹f_____ for her ²g_____ and also her ³s_____ clothes. Penélope is ⁴i_____ and she speaks four languages – Spanish, Italian, French and English. Her ⁵f_____ has helped her to appear in adverts on TV and in magazines.
Andy Murray was born in Glasgow, Scotland, in 1987. As a young boy, he was a ⁶s_____ tennis player and a good footballer, but he decided to play professional tennis. Murray is an exciting player to watch. He's got a lot of ⁷s_____ in his arms and can hit the ball very hard. He also thinks carefully on the tennis court and uses his ⁸i_____ and ⁹c_____ to win.

3 ⭐⭐ **Complete the sentences using the adjective or noun forms of the words in brackets.**

Is your brother ___intelligent___? (intelligence)

1 Beyoncé is a singer with great _____. (talented)
2 That actress has a big _____. (egotistical)
3 Do you want to be _____ in the future? (fame)
4 Playing basketball isn't easy. You need _____. (skilful)
5 Jennifer Aniston is a _____ celebrity. (style)
6 Singers need _____ when they perform in a concert. (courageous)
7 Asafa Powell is a _____ 100m runner. (strength)

4 ⭐⭐⭐ **Complete the text using words in exercises 1–3.**

Reach Sports Academy

Are you between the ages of 11 and 16? Reach Sports Academy is looking for ___talented___ young footballers, tennis players and runners.

Reach is an academy in Liverpool which mixes academic lessons with special classes in a variety of different sports. Past students at our academy include a number of very ¹_____ TV sports personalities.

We have places for new students to start at the academy next September. To get a place at the academy you need to:

• be a very good sportsperson and have a lot of ²_____ in two or more sports.
• be healthy and ³_____.
• work well alone and show ⁴_____. You must have your own ideas!
• be good team players and not be ⁵_____.
• have ⁶_____ and not be frightened to work hard to succeed.

LANGUAGE FOCUS ● *for* and *since* • Present perfect and past simple

4

for and *since*

1 ★ Complete the phrases with *for* or *since*.

for three weeks

1 _____ this morning
2 _____ one o'clock
3 _____ ten years
4 _____ 1995
5 _____ a few minutes
6 _____ eight months
7 _____ a short time
8 _____ last night
9 _____ five hours
10 _____ January
11 _____ seven days
12 _____ the 1960s

2 ★★ Write questions and answers using *for* and *since*.

how long / you / be / in this band (three years)
<u>How long have you been in this band?</u>
<u>I've been in this band for three years.</u>

1 how long / he / play / the drums (he was six)
_____
_____

2 how long / we / have / that piano (four months)
_____
_____

3 how long / they / study / music (many years)
_____
_____

4 how long / Maria / work with the band (last year)
_____
_____

5 how long / that singer / live / in New York (2010)
_____
_____

6 how long / you / like / the *Sugababes* (a long time)
_____
_____

7 how long / he / work / at the record company (November)
_____
_____

Present perfect and past simple

3 ★★ Complete the sentences using the present perfect or the past simple form of the verbs in the box.

> not see ~~have~~ finish play
> not listen walk live

My favourite singer ___has had___ three hits this summer.

1 I _____ that book on Wednesday. The ending was very good.
2 She loves her flat. She _____ there for five years.
3 Jack isn't in class today. We _____ him for a few days.
4 _____ you ever _____ rugby or basketball?
5 They _____ to that concert on the radio last night.
6 _____ he _____ to school with his friends yesterday?

4 ★★★ Choose the correct verb in brackets and complete the letter using the present perfect or the past simple.

Hi Jake,
We've **ve been** (be / wait) in London for four days and I don't want to go home! We ¹_____ (arrive / leave) here on Tuesday and since then we ²_____ (play / do) a lot of things. I ³_____ (go / visit) a number of different places – Big Ben, art galleries and museums. And guess what? My brother ⁴_____ (be / say) nice all the time and he ⁵_____ (not listen / not say) anything horrible yet!
   Yesterday we ⁶_____ (go / visit) to see a *Coldplay* concert at Wembley Arena. It ⁷_____ (become / start) at eight o'clock and the band ⁸_____ (play / be) really well.
   We still ⁹_____ (not go / not like) to the British Museum and we ¹⁰_____ (not want / not take) a boat trip on the river yet, but I think we're going to do that tomorrow.
   Love Chloe

Fame ■ 35

1 ★ Read the text. Tick ✓ the correct box.

The text is about …

a ☐ a teenage festival in a famous London club.
b ☐ a cheaper music festival for teenagers in a park.
c ☐ an expensive festival in Victoria Park, London.

A new type of festival

For most teenagers in the UK, it's difficult and expensive to get into pop festivals. The shows finish very late and the tickets sometimes cost more than £100. But things have started to change and that's because of the Underage Festival.

The festival was the idea of Sam Kilcoyne. Sam first started the Underage Club when he was fourteen because teenagers couldn't get into normal clubs to see live music. His club in London was incredibly successful, so he decided to have an Underage Festival, too.

This one-day festival for young people began in 2007 and it's become bigger every year since then. Talented bands and singers like Dizzee Rascal, Foals and Mystery Jets have appeared on the main stage.

The event takes place every August in Victoria Park in London. There's usually a long queue of really excited teenagers waiting for the gates to open at eleven o'clock. Ticket prices are much cheaper than for normal festivals.

Perhaps the most surprising thing about the festival is that adults can't go in at all. The event is only open to teenagers between the ages of fourteen and eighteen. Parents need to leave their teenagers at the gate and come back at eight o'clock when it's finished!

2 ★★ Find the words in the text and match them with the definitions.

1 live music — a a type of door where you go into a garden or park
2 successful
3 stage ⌐ b music that isn't recorded
4 takes place c happens
5 gate d popular, making a lot of money
　　　　　 e the thing musicians stand on when they play

3 ★★ Read the text again. Choose the correct answers.

It's often _____ for teenagers to get into festivals.

(a expensive) b cheap c easy

1 Sam was _____ when he began his club.
　a eleven b fourteen c eighteen
2 The Underage Festival lasts for _____.
　a a single day b eight days c eleven days
3 Since 2007, the festival has been _____ every year.
　a more expensive b later c larger
4 To get into the festival, people wait in a _____.
　a park b queue c club
5 _____ can't go into the festival.
　a Fourteen-year-olds b Eighteen-year-olds
　c Parents

4 ★★★ Answer the questions. Write complete sentences.

How much does it cost to see some shows?
The tickets sometimes cost more than £100.

1 Why did Sam start the Underage Club?
　_____
2 Where was the first Underage Club?
　_____
3 Which singers or bands have played at the Underage Festival?
　_____
4 In which month does the festival happen?
　_____
5 What time does the festival start and finish?
　_____
6 Why can't parents go to the festival with their children?
　_____

Build your vocabulary

5 ★★ Make new words using a prefix or a suffix in the box.

-able　-less　un-　-ful

useless

1 sleep_____ 　　4 success_____
2 _____creative 　5 point_____
3 _____kind 　　　6 predict_____

4

Language point: Order of adjectives

1 ⭐ Rewrite the sentences. Put the adjectives in brackets in the correct place.

That singer lives in a nice house. (big)
That singer lives in a nice, big house.

1 My favourite actor has got dark hair. (short)

2 You're wearing a long T-shirt. (black)

3 Miley Cyrus is in a new film. (strange)

4 It's a famous book. (old)

5 He's a confident boy. (little)

6 We've got a red car. (new)

2 ⭐⭐ Order the words to make sentences.

singer / talented / new / she's / a
She's a talented, new singer.

1 eyes / got / you've / green / big / wonderful

2 watching / excellent / DVD / old / we're / an

3 brown / got / small / Anna / a / dog / has

4 singer / he's / modern / stylish / a

5 long / she's / black / got / hair / nice

6 boy / young / Adam / a / is / shy

☐ TASK

3 ⭐⭐ Read the notes about Uncle Ben, then complete the biography.

Paragraph 1: dance teacher / Ireland / born in small old town near Dublin in the 1970s

Paragraph 2: be involved in the world of dance / since be / little boy

first study modern dance at four / start to appear on stage soon after that

big break / in 1979 / win a local children's talent show

Paragraph 3: at eighteen move to Manchester / study dance and drama at the university

live in Manchester since then / teach hip hop dance to teenagers at big modern school

My Uncle Ben is _a dance teacher_ .
He comes [1]_____
and he [2]_____ in
the 1970s.

Uncle Ben [3]_____
since [4]_____. He
[5]_____ at the age
of four and he [6]_____
_____ soon after
that. His [7]_____
in 1979 when he [8]_____
_____.

At the age of eighteen, he [9]_____
_____ and he
[10]_____.
He [11]_____.
He [12]_____
at a big modern school.

4 ⭐⭐⭐ Write a biography of a friend or relative. Use the text in exercise 3 to help you.

VOCABULARY AND LANGUAGE FOCUS
● Adjectives: personality

1 Complete the words in the sentences.

1 My brother doesn't like meeting my friends. He's really s _ _.
2 I want a good job. I'm quite a _ _ _ _ _ _ _ _.
3 She isn't very generous. She's a bit m _ _ _.
4 You always think about other people's feelings. You're kind and s _ _ _ _ _ _ _.
5 He never laughs. He's incredibly s _ _ _ _ _ _.
6 They listen to other people and try to understand them. They're very t _ _ _ _ _ _ _.
7 Are you happy and c _ _ _ _ _ _ _ _ all the time?
8 Sam asks lots of questions. He's c _ _ _ _ _ _.

2 Choose the correct words.

1 My brother is **really / a bit** intelligent. He took his exams a year early.
2 That actor is **not very / quite** talented. He didn't get the job.
3 Hollywood stars usually wear **very / a bit** expensive clothes.
4 I don't really like meeting new people. I'm usually **not very / quite** shy.
5 She won the talent show. There were a lot of people at the auditions. She was **a bit / incredibly** lucky.
6 We were **not very / a bit** hungry after the show so we went to a restaurant.

I can describe people's personalities.
MY EVALUATION ▢▢▢▢

READING ● Celebrity culture

3 Complete the sentences. Add a prefix or a suffix to the words in brackets.

1 The singer went on a _____ (world) tour last year.
2 She had a lot of _____ (sleep) nights travelling from city to city.
3 It was a very _____ (success) tour with big audiences.
4 It was _____ (predict) that her wonderful new song sold a lot of copies in many countries.
5 Some people were _____ (kind) and said that her song wasn't very exciting.

I can understand a text about fame.
MY EVALUATION ▢▢▢▢

LANGUAGE FOCUS ● Present perfect
+ still, just, yet and already

4 Complete the sentences with still, just, yet or already.

1 Peter _____ hasn't arrived home. He's late!
2 We haven't seen the new Bond film _____.
3 She looks happy! She's _____ won a big prize.
4 Where's the chocolate?
   I'm sorry. I've _____ finished it. I ate it all last week!
5 Are you hungry?
   No, I've _____ eaten dinner. I only had it a minute ago.
6 He hasn't appeared on TV _____, but he's going to be in a show next month.
7 Let's go to Rome for our holiday.
   No, I've _____ been there. I went three years ago.

I can talk about things that people have done.
MY EVALUATION ▢▢▢▢

VOCABULARY AND LISTENING ● Nouns and adjectives: personal qualities

5 Complete the sentences with the words in the box.

> independence   lucky   skill   creative
> style   egotistical   courage

1 The students at the art college wear very interesting and attractive clothes. They've got a lot of _____.
2 It's good for you to learn to look after yourself. You must have some _____.
3 One new girl sang a song on her own to two hundred people. It took a lot of _____ to do that.
4 People think it's easy to be a dancer, but you must have _____ to dance well.
5 He wasn't a very good singer. He was very _____ to win a place at the school.
6 That pop star thinks she's incredibly important. She's very _____.
7 All the students are very _____; they're always thinking of new ideas.

> **I can understand an interview about a creative school.**
>
> MY EVALUATION ☐ ☐ ☐ ☐

LANGUAGE FOCUS ● *for* and *since*

6 Write sentences using the present perfect and *for* or *since*.

1 he / live / in Hollywood / October
_____
2 she / not release / an album / three years
_____
3 they / study / English / 2007
_____
4 he / play / with this band / last year
_____
5 you / know / that singer / six months
_____
6 I / listen / hip hop music / a long time
_____

> **I can talk about things I have read, heard or seen.**
>
> MY EVALUATION ☐ ☐ ☐ ☐

SPEAKING ● Identifying and describing people

7 Match sentence halves 1–7 with a–g.

1	Who are you	a	boy over there?
2	Who's that	b	like someone famous.
3	Which one? The boy with	c	interesting face.
		d	looking at?
4	What about	e	know him?
5	He looks	f	him?
6	He's got an	g	the short dark hair?
7	Do you		

> **I can identify and describe people.**
>
> MY EVALUATION ☐ ☐ ☐ ☐

WRITING ● A biography

8 Complete the text with the words in the box.

> involved   then   good-looking   since
> long   personality   born   break   winners

Cheryl Cole was [1]_____ in the north of England in 1983. She's really [2]_____ with dark brown eyes and lovely [3]_____ hair. She's got a very friendly [4]_____, but she's also quite determined.

Cheryl has been [5]_____ in show business [6]_____ she was a child. She studied dance and she appeared as a model in a number of adverts.

Her big [7]_____ came in 2002 when she was one of the [8]_____ of the TV talent show *Popstars – the Rivals*. On the show she became part of the group *Girls Aloud*. Since [9]_____, she has had many hits with them. More recently she has had hits as a solo singer. She now appears as a judge next to Simon Cowell on the programme *The X Factor*.

> **I can write a biography of a celebrity.**
>
> MY EVALUATION ☐ ☐ ☐ ☐

VOCABULARY ● School life: verbs

1 ★ Match 1–9 with a–i.

1	copy	**a** an exam
2	play	**b** in exams
3	cheat	**c** a friend's work
4	revise	**d** school
5	take / fail / pass	**e** truant
6	get	**f** someone
7	leave	**g** for a test
8	make	**h** friends
9	bully / expel / suspend	**i** bad / good marks / a qualification

2 ★★ Choose the correct answers to complete the text.

Marcus Garvey Comprehensive School, Dorridge

_____ good qualifications and ¹_____ friends at Marcus Garvey School!

At Marcus Garvey School, we think it is very important for students to get good ²_____ during the school year and to ³_____ for their end-of-year exams. Students ⁴_____ the exams in June and 87% of our students ⁵_____ and go on to get good jobs when they leave ⁶_____.

	a Take	**b** Get	**c** Pass
1	**a** make	**b** take	**c** play
2	**a** marks	**b** homework	**c** tests
3	**a** pass	**b** do	**c** revise
4	**a** take	**b** get	**c** revise
5	**a** make	**b** pass	**c** fail
6	**a** school	**b** work	**c** homework

3 ★★ Complete the sentences using the past simple form of the verbs in exercise 1.

She ___**passed**___ the exam. She got 100%!

1 Those boys were horrible. They _____ younger children.
2 They _____ for the exam every evening.
3 He _____ some new friends at the football club.
4 He _____ the exam. He got 20%.
5 She _____ in the maths exam, so the teacher _____ her.
6 He _____ truant and the teacher told his parents.
7 She _____ her friend's homework, but the teacher knew.
8 My brother _____ school last year and now he's at university.

4 ★★★ Answer the questions. Write complete sentences.

What marks do you usually get for maths?
I usually get bad / good marks for maths.

1 What marks do you usually get for English?
_____
_____

2 Where do you usually do your homework?
_____
_____

3 When and how do you revise for exams?
_____
_____

4 How can people cheat in exams?
_____
_____

5 At what age can students leave school in your country?
_____
_____

6 Do you enjoy school? What do you enjoy about it?
_____
_____

should and *must*

1 ⭐ Complete the sentences with *mustn't* or *should*.

How ___*should*___ I answer this question?

1 I _____ text friends in class.

2 You _____ revise before the English test. -

3 We _____ go home before it gets dark.

4 You _____ fail these exams. They're very important.

5 Your dad _____ stop smoking. It's unhealthy.

6 You _____ shout in the library.

7 You _____ copy people's work.

8 _____ I tell the teacher about the bully?

2 ⭐⭐ Complete the sentences with the verbs in the box.

> mustn't have   should be   ~~must wear~~
> mustn't eat   mustn't run   should bring
> must study   must be

SCHOOL RULES

Girls ___*must wear*___ skirts and black shoes.

1 Boys _____ long hair.

2 In the winter, students _____ hats and raincoats. Please do not wear baseball caps.

3 You _____ inside the school, it's dangerous. Please walk.

4 You _____ anything in the classrooms. Please have your lunch in the canteen or outside.

5 Students _____ polite to the teachers. Students will be suspended for bad behaviour.

6 All students _____ English and maths. These subjects are compulsory.

7 Morning classes start at 8.45 a.m. Students _____ in school by 8.30 a.m., if possible.

---

have to and *don't have to*

3 ⭐⭐ Complete the sentences using the correct form of *have to* or *don't have to* and the verbs in the box.

> do   get   go   revise   play   wear   ~~work~~

My dad ___*has to work*___ on Saturdays.

1 She _____ for the test because she isn't studying geography.

2 We _____ a uniform, but we can wear jeans on Fridays.

3 She _____ good marks because she wants to go to college.

4 They _____ to school today. It's a school holiday.

5 _____ Alan _____ football after school?

6 His new school is really strict. He _____ homework every evening, including Fridays.

4 ⭐⭐⭐ Write sentences about you and people in your family. Use the words in the box or your own ideas.

> wash the car   clean the windows
> go to work   visit my grandparents
> make the dinner   tidy my room
> look after my brother / sister

1 Write three things that you / they have to do this weekend.

I have to tidy my room. My brother has to wash
the car. _____
_____
_____
_____

2 Write three things that you / they don't have to do this weekend.

_____
_____
_____
_____

3 Write three things that you / they have to do every Monday morning.

_____
_____
_____
_____

VOCABULARY ● School life: nouns

1 ⭐ **Choose the correct words.**

My brother eats and sleeps at his school. He doesn't come home every day because it's a (boarding)/ **mixed** school.

1 My parents don't have to pay for my school. I go to a **state** / **private** school.
2 My sister is 16. She goes to the same **primary** / **secondary** school as me.
3 We don't have to wear a school **subject** / **uniform** at my school.
4 Children in England go to **primary** / **private** school between the ages of four and ten.
5 My brother can't go to the same school as me and my sister. My sister and I go to a **single-sex** / **mixed** school.
6 The **school-leaving age** / **school rule** in a lot of countries is 16.

2 ⭐⭐ **Complete the text with the words in the box.**

> school-leaving age   private school
> school subjects   school uniform
> school holidays   primary school
> state school   secondary school

Schools in England

Children in England usually start _primary school_ when they're five years old. Their parents can choose between a ¹_____, which is free, or a ²_____, which they have to pay for. At the age of eleven, students start ³_____. Students have to study English, maths and science. Other ⁴_____ include modern foreign languages, history, geography, art and design technology.

The ⁵_____ is sixteen, but many students continue for two extra years and take 'A-levels' before they go to university.

The school year starts in September and the main ⁶_____ are at Christmas, Easter and in the summer. A lot of schools have a ⁷_____, but some schools allow students to wear their own clothes.

3 ⭐⭐ **Write words for the definitions.**

A school, usually private, where students live.
boarding school

1 A school for both boys and girls...
_____
2 Clothes which students have to wear at school.
_____
3 A school for only boys or only girls.
_____
4 A school for students aged 11 to 18.
_____
5 The age when students can stop going to school.
_____
6 The list of things that you have to or mustn't do at school.
_____
7 The weeks when you don't have to go to school.
_____
8 A school which you have to pay for.
_____

4 ⭐⭐⭐ **Answer the questions. Write complete sentences.**

Do you go to a primary or a secondary school?
I go to a secondary school.

1 How old were you when you started your primary school? When did you leave?
_____
2 How long have you been at secondary school? What is the school-leaving age?
_____
3 Do you go to a state school or a private school?
_____
4 Do you have to wear a uniform at your school? If yes, describe it.
_____
5 When are your school holidays and how long are they?
_____
6 What are some of your school rules?
_____

should, must and *have to*

1 ★ Choose the correct answers.

He _____ cycle to school. It's cheaper than the bus.

(**a** should) **b** shouldn't **c** mustn't

1 My dad _____ start work at eight o'clock.
   a has to **b** have to **c** should

2 I _____ remember to finish my homework.
   a doesn't have to **b** must **c** shouldn't

3 I _____ get up at six o'clock on Mondays.
   I hate Mondays!
   a mustn't **b** have to **c** has to

4 You _____ be late. It's rude.
   a don't have to **b** must **c** shouldn't

5 We _____ leave now. We can leave later.
   a mustn't **b** should **c** don't have to

6 You _____ copy my homework! It isn't fair!
   a mustn't **b** don't have to **c** should

7 Marc _____ do the washing-up. He's already done it three times this week.
   a doesn't have to **b** mustn't **c** has to

2 ★★ Complete the text with the verbs in the box.

> must mustn't should mustn't
> ~~don't have to~~ should

Welcome to Jordan Hill Tennis Club

During matches
- There are chairs next to each tennis court. You **don't have to** stand. You ¹_____ arrive early to get a good seat.
- You ²_____ take photographs.

Food and drink
- You ³_____ eat or drink in the stadium. You ⁴_____ have your food and drinks in the café.

Crime
- You should be careful with your things. You ⁵_____ always leave your jackets and bags with somebody.

3 ★★ Complete the sentences using *should, must* or *have to* and the correct form of the verbs in brackets.

Henry can relax. He **doesn't have to do** (do) the exam.

1 You _____ (drop) litter. You _____ (use) the bins.

2 You're tired. You _____ (rest) for a while.

3 Hurry up! We _____ (leave) soon. It's nearly dark.

4 They're lucky. They _____ (get up) early.

5 You _____ (write) something. It can be anything. It _____ (be) perfect.

6 You _____ (bully) people.

7 Someone _____ (go) to the shop before we can have breakfast. We've eaten all the bread.

8 You _____ (visit) London one day.

4 ★★★ Complete the sentences using the correct form of *should, must* or *have to* and your own ideas.

It's raining.

You **should stay at home.**

1 You look tired.
   You _____

2 It's Saturday!
   We _____

3 The rules about smoking are clear.
   You _____

4 Josh is hungry.
   He _____

5 That book's too expensive.
   You _____

6 There's a uniform at my new school.
   We _____

7 The film starts at 6 p.m. It's 5.30 p.m.
   You _____

8 She's done her homework.
   She _____

1 ⭐ Read the interview quickly. Tick ✓ the correct box.

How many subjects is Anwen studying?

a ☐ Seven **b** ☐ Nine **c** ☐ Eleven

Boarding School

Mr Lee Why do you go to a boarding school?

Anwen My parents are musicians. They work in a different country every month. It's difficult for me to go to a normal secondary school, so I go to a boarding school in Swansea.

Mr Lee Could you describe a typical day at your school?

Anwen We have to get up at seven o'clock. We have classes and activities all day from 8.30 a.m. to 5 p.m. In the evenings, we don't have to do anything. We can watch films, we can chat with our friends and eat sweets and biscuits, or we can chat on our mobile phones. We must be in bed by ten-thirty. 'Lights out' is at eleven o'clock.

Mr Lee What subjects do you have to study?

Anwen Private schools don't have to follow the National Curriculum, but everyone at my school must study English, maths, science and also Welsh, because our school is in Wales.

Mr Lee Do you have to study any other subjects?

Anwen Well, the other subjects aren't compulsory. I'm studying citizenship, history, music, PE and French. There's also Personal Social and Health Education. In PSHE, we learn about health and society. I get good marks, but I hate it. It's boring!

Mr Lee Do you like your boarding school?

Anwen Absolutely. The head teacher is good and I like the school. But we have to wear a school uniform.

Mr Lee Are there any disadvantages?

Anwen We have to study harder than students in some state secondary schools and we can't say, 'I've left my homework at home' because we live at school!

2 ⭐⭐ Read the text again. Write *true* or *false*.

Swansea is in Wales.   <u>true</u>

1 Anwen lives with her parents.   _____

2 She goes to a state secondary school. _____

3 She starts school at 7 a.m.   _____

4 She can choose what she wants to do in the evenings. _____

5 She has to study English and maths.   _____

6 All students have to study citizenship. _____

3 ⭐⭐⭐ Answer the questions. Write complete sentences.

Why does Anwen go to a boarding school?

<u>Her parents always work in different countries,</u>

<u>so she can't go to a normal school.</u>

1 What time does Anwen have to go to sleep?

_____

2 How many compulsory subjects are there?

_____

3 How many languages does Anwen have to study?

_____

4 What subject doesn't Anwen like? Why not?

_____

5 What are the disadvantages of boarding schools?

_____

Build your vocabulary

4 ⭐⭐ Complete the text with American English words.

It's difficult for me to go to a normal __*high school*__ (secondary school), so I go to a boarding school.

My favorite subjects are French and math, and I get good ¹_____ (marks).

After classes, we can watch ²_____ (films), we can chat with our friends and eat ³_____ (sweets) and ⁴_____ (biscuits). I sometimes chat with my family on my ⁵_____ (mobile phone).

The ⁶_____ (head teacher) is good.

Language point: Ordering information

1 ⭐ Order the words in the box.

> Finally   Firstly   Secondly

1 _____
2 _____
3 _____

2 ⭐⭐ Write the sentences as one paragraph. Add the words in exercise 1 and *also*.

1 it's quicker than a letter
2 it's easier to type than to write, and you can add attachments
3 it's better for the environment

Why email is a good idea

Firstly, email is a good idea because _____
_____
_____
_____
_____
_____
_____
_____
_____
_____
_____
_____

☐ TASK

3 ⭐⭐ Read the essay title and the notes. Complete the opinion essay.

Are you in favour of exams or against them?

schools: exams test students' progress

not in favour – several reasons:

1 some students good in class – get nervous – not get good marks

2 students remember facts for a short while – not understand the subject

3 exams should be realistic – outside school, people can use dictionaries / calculators

Conclusion: essays and project work better than exams

Are you in favour of exams or against them?

Most schools use ____exams____ to test
1_____, but I'm
2_____ of exams for
3_____. In my opinion, there are three reasons why schools shouldn't use exams.
    Firstly, some students are 4_____
_____, but 5_____
_____, so they never 6_____
_____. Secondly, I think it's a bad thing to train students to remember 7_____
_____. Students who get good marks in exams are good at exams, but they don't have to
8_____. Finally, I think that 9_____. In most exams, you can't use a dictionary or a calculator. But in the real world, people can 10_____
_____ all the time.
    So all in all, I think that 11_____
are more effective tests than exams.

4 ⭐⭐⭐ Read the essay question. Make notes. Then write an opinion essay.

Are you in favour of compulsory school for students under the age of sixteen or against it?

MY EVALUATION   Check your progress. Do the exercises and then complete your own evaluation.

☐☐☐☐ I need to try this again.   ☐☐☐☐ I am happy with this.

☐☐☐☐ I could do this better.   ☐☐☐☐ I can do this very well.

VOCABULARY AND LANGUAGE FOCUS ●
School life: verbs

1 Complete the dialogue with the words in the box.

> cheated   copied   expel   got good marks
> passed   play truant   suspended

Austin	Where's Caleb?
Nathan	The head teacher [1]_____ him yesterday.
Austin	Why? Did he [2]_____ again?
Nathan	No, he [3]_____ Anna's homework.
Austin	Why did he do that? He [4]_____ in the exam last month. He did well.
Nathan	Caleb only [5]_____ that exam because he [6]_____!
Austin	Really? Will the school [7]_____ him?
Nathan	Maybe. I'm not sure.

2 Write school rules using *should, must* or *mustn't*.

1 we / help / new students

_____

2 we / copy / our friends' work

_____

3 we / be / friendly to everybody

_____

4 we / text / during classes

_____

5 we / do / our homework

_____

6 we / get / to classes on time

_____

> **I can talk about school rules.**
> MY EVALUATION   ☐☐☐☐

READING ● Cheating

3 Read the email. Write the British English words for the American English words in bold.

> Dear Ali
> Thank you for your email. I'm sorry to hear about your friend. Yes, sometimes students at my [1]**high school** cheat in exams to get better [2]**grades**, too. I agree with you that it's really bad. Some students use their [3]**cell phones** to check the answers or keep the answers in their [4]**pants**, and some students copy their friend's work. The [5]**principal** always takes cheating very seriously. Last year, two kids were suspended. Now they work in the local [6]**store**. Write soon, Tod

1 _____   3 _____   5 _____

2 _____   4 _____   6 _____

> **I can give my opinions about cheating at school.**
> MY EVALUATION   ☐☐☐☐

LANGUAGE FOCUS ● *have to* and *don't have to*

4 Write about your own rules at home and at school. Use *have to* and *don't have to*.

> clean the classroom   do a test every day
> make my bed   do the washing-up
> watch the news   wear a uniform

At home _____

_____

_____.

At school _____

_____

_____.

> **I can talk about rules at home and at school.**
> MY EVALUATION   ☐☐☐☐

VOCABULARY AND LISTENING ● School life: nouns

5 Complete the words in the text.

I go to a ¹s _ _ _ _ _-s _ _ school for girls.

It's a ²s _ _ _ _ s _ _ _ _ _, it isn't a ³p _ _ _ _ _ _ s _ _ _ _ _. I like my school. My favourite ⁴s _ _ _ _ _ s _ _ _ _ _ _ are history and English. The best thing about school is the ⁵s _ _ _ _ _ h _ _ _ _ _ _ _! We always go to the beach in the summer.

I don't like everything about school. We have to wear a ⁶s _ _ _ _ _ u _ _ _ _ _ _. I hate it!

> **I can understand people talking about schools.**
> MY EVALUATION ☐☐☐☐

LANGUAGE FOCUS ● should, must and have to

6 Choose the correct words.

1 In Britain, students **must / don't have to** leave school when they are 16. Some stay until they're 18.
2 We **have to / shouldn't** be quiet in the library.
3 She can take the exam again next year. She **must / shouldn't** be upset.
4 Students **should / mustn't** work hard at school to get good marks.
5 We **shouldn't / must** go to all of our lessons.
6 My school **shouldn't / mustn't** have so many rules. It's too strict.

> **I can compare my school to schools in other countries.**
> MY EVALUATION ☐☐☐☐

SPEAKING ● Asking for and giving advice

7 Complete the dialogue with the words in the box.

> sure   matter   should   think   whatever

Nina What's the ¹_____?
Jon I played truant last week.
Nina Why?
Jon Alastair Lane was bullying me. What ²_____ I do?
Nina ³_____ you do, don't play truant! That's for ⁴_____.
Jon Yes, you're right.
Nina I ⁵_____ you should talk to your parents and the head teacher.
Jon Maybe you're right. Thank you, Nina.

> **I can ask for and give advice.**
> MY EVALUATION ☐☐☐☐

WRITING ● An opinion essay

8 Choose the correct answers and complete the text.

In some schools, students have to do PE. Some students love PE, and that's great, but I hate PE. ¹_____, education should be about the mind, not the body. ²_____ compulsory PE lessons ³_____. Firstly, sport is very competitive. For students who are tall or fast, that's great. But ⁴_____ make students compete if they don't want to. Secondly, it is expensive to buy special new clothes. Finally, PE makes students really tired. ⁵_____, PE shouldn't be a compulsory school subject.

1 a For various reasons   b In my opinion   c In conclusion
2 a I'm not in favour of   b All in all   c In conclusion
3 a I'm in favour   b for several reasons   c I'm against
4 a in conclusion   b I'm in favour of   c I think that it's a bad thing to
5 a For several reasons   b I'm not in favour of   c In conclusion

> **I can write an opinion essay.**
> MY EVALUATION ☐☐☐☐

VOCABULARY ● Action and protest

1 ★ Find nine more words.

P	U	B	L	I	C	I	Z	E
E	P	R	O	T	E	S	T	C
T	X	K	V	U	M	L	Y	A
I	C	O	L	L	E	C	T	M
T	M	J	W	B	E	R	M	P
I	A	R	Y	A	T	N	I	A
O	R	G	A	N	I	Z	E	I
N	C	J	Q	Z	V	B	P	G
K	H	D	O	N	A	T	E	N

publicize

1 _____ 5 _____
2 _____ 6 _____
3 _____ 7 _____
4 _____ 8 _____
        9 _____

2 ★★ Read the definitions and complete the words.

The help that you give to an organization or charity. s_upport_

1 A person or company that gives money so that an event can happen. s_____

2 A type of protest where people stop buying a product. b_____

3 A rule which says that people can't do something. b_____

4 To go to a place at a certain time to see and talk to other people. m_____

5 A group of people who walk through a town to protest about something. m_____

6 A plan to fight something you don't agree with. c_____

7 A piece of paper with a lot of people's names on. It asks the government or another organization to change something. p_____

8 When a person puts information in the newspapers and on TV. p_____

9 When you say that you will do something that you do not have to do. v_____

3 ★★ Complete the sentences with the words in the box.

> protest   donation   campaign   organize
> ~~petition~~   boycott   collection   donate

People plan to __petition__ the government about the terrible roads.

1 Would you like to _____ some money to this hospital charity?

2 I'm angry about the new shopping centre. I want to join the _____ about it outside the town hall on Saturday.

3 They want to plan and _____ a big march through the centre of town.

4 He's got a large _____ of books.

5 That supermarket isn't paying enough to the coffee farmers. We're going to _____ it.

6 The local people want to _____ against the airport.

7 A rich businessman gave a big _____ to our campaign.

4 ★★★ Complete the text.

AFRICAN ADVENTURE

Eighteen-year-old Ben White has __organized__ a trip to Africa this summer. He wants to work as a ¹_____ there for six months.

Last year, Ben heard about an ²_____ called *Bikes for Africa*. He was interested in their campaign to ³_____ bikes and take them to children in South Africa. *Bikes for Africa* also helps children to learn all about the bikes.

At the moment, Ben needs money for his trip and he's looking for people to ⁴_____ him. If you're interested, you can ⁵_____ Ben at the library this Friday at five o'clock. You can also see him on the local TV news this Thursday. He's doing an interview to ⁶_____ the trip.

will and *might*

1 ⭐ Complete the table with the words in the box.

> might not   protest   won't   might
> 'll   Will

will	
Affirmative	
I / You / He / She / It / We / You / They ___'ll___ volunteer.	
Negative	
I / You / He / She / It / We / You / They ¹_____ march.	
Questions	
²_____ I / you / he / she / it / we / you / they ³_____?	
might	
Affirmative	
I / You / He / She / It / We / You / They ⁴_____ donate some money.	
Negative	
I / You / He / She / It / We / You / They ⁵_____ support the campaign.	

2 ⭐⭐ Complete the sentences using *might* (✓), *will* (✓✓), *might not* (✗), *won't* (✗✗) and the verbs in the box.

> donate   wait   like   volunteer   help
> get   go   come   ~~start~~

We ___might start___ a petition to ban cars from our town centre. ✓

1 In the future, I think I _____ for a children's charity. ✓✓

2 He isn't interested in the new campaign, so he _____ to the meeting. ✗✗

3 You _____ this DVD about the Amazon. It's quite interesting. ✓

4 She doesn't usually enjoy big concerts. She _____ a ticket. ✗

5 You must run for the bus. It definitely _____ for you. ✗✗

6 When the new sports centre is open, we _____ swimming there. ✓✓

7 It sounds like a good cause. I _____ some money. ✓✓

8 We're busy. We _____ to organize the protest. ✗

First conditional

3 ⭐⭐ Match phrases from A and B to write first conditional sentences. You will need to change the form of some of the verbs.

A	B
If ...	
we publicize the protest	we arrive on time
you ask everybody for £1	everybody come
David speak to the teachers	you collect lots of money
you not read our leaflet carefully	my mum be worried
my sister go on the march	they sign the petition
it rain on Saturday	you not understand it
we take the fast train	we take a big umbrella

If we publicize the protest, everybody will come.

1 _____

2 _____

3 _____

4 _____

5 _____

6 _____

4 ⭐⭐⭐ Complete the sentences using your own ideas.

If I have any free time in the future, I'll work as a volunteer and clean up our town.

1 If we don't protect the environment, _____.

2 The students at our school will protest if _____.

3 If the government bans violent video games, _____.

4 My mum will be worried if _____.

5 He'll come to the meeting if _____.

6 If we don't save the rainforest, _____.

1 ⭐ Look at the photos. Complete the phrases with the words in the box.

> find out   set up   carry on   look after
> ~~join in~~   sign up

join in_____ a protest

1 _____ information

2 _____ for something

3 _____ collecting money

4 _____ endangered plants

5 _____ a new animal hospital

2 ⭐⭐ Choose the correct answers.

I want to _____ for this monthly magazine about the environment.

a end up   b set up   **c sign up**   d find out

1 People might _____ tigers completely if they don't stop killing them.
a carry on   b look after   c find out   d wipe out

2 Don't stop campaigning. You must _____.
a sign up   b carry on   c join in   d set up

3 If we build houses everywhere, we'll _____ with no forests at all.
a end up   b sign up   c set up   d find out

4 Can you _____ our dog next week?
a wipe out   b find out   c carry on   d look after

5 Would you like to _____ our protest?
a look after   b wipe out   c join in   d end up

6 We want to _____ a new recycling centre.
a end up   b set up   c sign up   d find out

3 ⭐⭐ Complete the dialogues with the words in the box.

> join in   end up   wipe out   find out
> ~~set up~~   carry on   look after

What are you going to do in the future?
I'm going to ___set up___ a hospital in Africa.

1 Did you _____ the answer to the maths question?
Yes. It's 2,321.

2 How can I help your campaign?
You can _____ our meetings on Fridays.

3 Has she finished her homework already?
No, she has to _____ for another hour.

4 Why do you support that animal charity?
Because we might _____ many endangered animals in the future.

5 Come and play tennis with us!
I can't. I have to _____ my baby brother.

6 Do you think we can save Siberian tigers?
No, not really. I think we might _____ with only a few tigers in zoos.

4 ⭐⭐⭐ Complete the text with phrasal verbs in exercises 1–3.

Interested in the environment?
Then come and join us!

We are a group of teenagers who have ___set up___ a new organization to protect and
1_____ the environment in our area.

We think that if people 2_____ building new roads and houses, they might 3_____ many of the interesting birds, insects and animals which live in the countryside around our town. We might 4_____ with only a small number of different species.

We are looking for new members to 5_____ our weekend activities and conservation projects. If you want to 6_____ more about our organization or 7_____ for our monthly newsletter, please phone 004275 483282.

LANGUAGE FOCUS ● *be going to* and *will* • Present continuous for future arrangements

be going to and *will*

1 ⭐ Complete the table with the words in the box.

> 'm   aren't   's   Am   'm not
> Is   're   isn't   Are

be going to
Affirmative
I' _m_ going to visit the rainforest.
He / She / It ¹_____ going to wipe out plant species in the Amazon.
We / You / They ²_____ going to help.
Negative
I ³_____ going to march on Friday.
He / She / It ⁴_____ going to advertise the campaign.
We / You / They ⁵_____ going to volunteer.
Questions
⁶_____ I going to find out the answer?
⁷_____ he / she / it going to destroy the rainforest?
⁸_____ we / you / they going to collect money?

2 ⭐⭐ Match sentences 1–7 with plans and predictions a–g.

1 People are cutting down too many trees. _b_
2 We're angry about the new airport. ___
3 Rainforest birds are losing their home. ___
4 The scientist wants to visit the Amazon. ___
5 They're organizing a good campaign. ___
6 I've got a geography exam next week. ___
7 We're planning a big concert for next year. ___

a We're sure that a lot of people will come.
b The forest will disappear.
c They'll get a lot of support.
d We're going to protest about it on Friday.
e They will soon be in danger.
f I'm going to revise every evening.
g He's going to go there next year.

3 ⭐⭐ Complete the sentences with *will* or *be going to* and the verbs in brackets.

I can't come on the march tomorrow.
I _'m going to look after_ (look after) my sister.

1 In the future, I think humans _____ (wipe out) many different species.
2 He's buying some eggs because he _____ (make) a cake for the charity sale.
3 I haven't finished designing that leaflet. I'm sure I _____ (finish) it on time.
4 I'm making sandwiches because I _____ (have) a picnic with my friends later.
5 Don't go on holiday to that island. You _____ (not find) any nice beaches there.
6 Do your parents have any holiday plans? No, they _____ (not travel) anywhere this summer.

4 ⭐⭐⭐ Complete the sentences using *will* or *be going to* and your own ideas.

In five years' time, I _'ll be at university_____.

1 At the weekend, I _____.
2 When I'm 25, I _____.
3 This evening, my mum _____.
4 When my cousin is older _____ _____.
5 Tomorrow, my school friends _____ _____.
6 In ten years' time, my best friend _____ _____.

Present continuous for future arrangements

5 ⭐⭐ Write sentences about Jodie, Cara and Ben. Use the present continuous.

	Jodie and Cara	Ben
Friday evening	*meet Jane outside the cinema*	¹ *play in a football match*
Saturday afternoon	² *cook with friends*	³ *have a pizza with his best friend Mark*
Sunday morning	⁴ *watch a DVD*	⁵ *visit his grandparents*

On Friday evening Jodie and Cara are meeting Jane outside the cinema.

1 _____
2 _____
3 _____
4 _____
5 _____

1 (★) **Read the text. Tick ✓ the correct box.**

The text is about a charity which ...

a ☐ takes musicians to the rainforest.
b ☐ saves the rainforest and its people.
c ☐ helps farmers look after the rainforest.

The Rainforest Foundation UK

The Rainforest Foundation is a charity in the UK. It campaigns for the preservation of the world's rainforests and the rights of the people who live there. There are other *Rainforest Foundations* in the USA and Norway.

The musician Sting and his wife set up the charity in 1989 after they saw the unacceptable destruction of the Amazon rainforest. Some farmers were wiping out large parts of the forest, which is the home of indigenous people. *The Rainforest Foundation* thinks that indigenous people are very important to the rainforests, and the charity is going to carry on its work with them in the future.

The Rainforest Foundation has grown over the last twenty years and it now supports projects in different countries including Brazil, Peru, Cameroon and Uganda. Since it first started, the charity has helped local people to protect and save more than 100,000 square kilometres of the rainforest in a number of countries.

Every year, supporters of the charity join in a number of big events to collect money. This year, they're going to run the London Marathon again. If you look at *The Rainforest Foundation* webpage, you'll find information about their latest events and campaigns. You can also sign up for an email newsletter.

2 (★★) **Read the text again. Write *true* or *false*.**

The Rainforest Foundation only campaigns to save the Amazon rainforest.   __false__

1 Sting set up the foundation with some farmers.   _____
2 The charity started in 1989.   _____
3 The charity is going to stop working with indigenous people.   _____
4 In the past twenty years the charity has become bigger.   _____
5 The charity supports projects in Norway.   _____
6 Supporters of *The Rainforest Foundation* are going to compete in the London Marathon.   _____

3 (★★★) **Answer the questions. Write complete sentences.**

What does *The Rainforest Foundation UK* campaign for?

__It campaigns for the preservation of the world's__
__rainforests and the rights of its people.__

1 Where can you find two other *Rainforest Foundations*?
_____
_____

2 Why did Sting and his wife start the charity?
_____
_____

3 Where does *The Rainforest Foundation* have projects?
_____
_____

4 How much rainforest has the charity saved?
_____
_____

5 How can you find out more about *The Rainforest Foundation*?
_____
_____

Build your vocabulary

4 (★★) **Complete the words with the negative prefixes *un-*, *in-* or *im-*.**

1 Many families throw away a lot of food. It's really ____necessary and ____acceptable.
2 Campaigners are becoming ____patient with the supermarkets. They think it's ____sane to throw away so much food. Customers need to learn to eat ____perfect fruit.
3 It's probably ____practical to think that we can stop them building the new road.
4 My brother eats a lot of ____healthy food.
5 I felt ____happy because my friend said my haircut was terrible! It was an ____kind and ____sensitive thing to say.

Language point: Explaining

1 ⭐ Choose the correct words.

We don't agree with your campaign. We have **because** / (**therefore**) decided not to sign the petition.

1 We think that trains are better than cars **as** / **therefore** they produce less pollution.
2 **As** / **For this reason**, we need to support this charity.
3 I didn't buy that writing paper **because** / **therefore** I didn't have enough money.
4 **As** / **Therefore** you were out when we called, we have decided to write you a letter.
5 He isn't going to join in the march **for this reason** / **because** he's playing football tomorrow.
6 We don't agree with motorways **as** / **for this reason** they are bad for the environment.
7 We're unhappy about the situation and we have **as** / **therefore** decided to protest.

2 ⭐⭐ Match sentences 1–4 with a–d. Then write sentences with *as*, *because* or *for this reason*.

1 The letter is important.
2 We're going to meet some politicians.
3 You didn't write a letter to the newspaper.
4 She isn't going to join in your campaign.

a She doesn't support your ideas.
b We didn't get any publicity.
c We're going to read it carefully.
d We want to talk about nuclear power.

1 *The letter is important. For this reason, we're going to read it carefully.*
2 _____
_____
3 _____
_____
4 _____
_____

☐ TASK

3 ⭐⭐ Read the notes for Hannah's email. Then complete the email.

NOTES:

Paragraph 1
I / email / you / because / I / just / join a group

Paragraph 2
we / be / concerned / the open-air swimming pool in town

if / it / close / there / be / nowhere / for teenagers to go

Paragraph 3
therefore / we / decide / to set up / campaign

we / be going to / have party / sell cakes / collect money

Paragraph 4
you know / a lot of people there

Hi Nathan

How are you? **I'm emailing you because** _____ I've just joined a group called 'Save Our Pool' and I thought you might be interested in it.

It's a group of young people and ¹_____
_____.

The local council is going to shut it soon.
²_____

for teenagers to go.

³_____

to save the pool. ⁴_____
at my house at four o'clock on Saturday afternoon
and ⁵_____.

I hope you can come to the party as it will be
good fun. ⁶_____.

Love

Hannah

4 ⭐⭐⭐ Imagine that you have just joined a campaign. Write an email and invite a friend to a party or disco to raise money. Use the text in exercise 3 to help you.

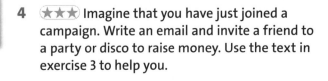

VOCABULARY AND LANGUAGE FOCUS ●
Action and protest

1 Complete the sentences with the words in the box.

> march   ban   collect   petition
> sponsor   meeting   volunteer

1 We want to write our names on the _____ against the airport.

2 Are you running in the marathon to get money for the hospital? I'll _____ you if you want.

3 Are you going to the _____ in the town hall tonight?

4 When I'm older I want to work as a _____ in Africa.

5 There's a protest on Tuesday and we might _____ through the streets of our city.

6 We will _____ a lot of money if we have a cake sale.

7 I think the government will definitely _____ smoking in public places.

2 Complete the sentences with *will* or *might*.

1 I _____ definitely organize a protest if they decide to build this new road.

2 Shall we organize a petition? It _____ help. I'm not sure.

3 Mark _____ make some posters for the meeting. Let's ask him and see.

4 I think the best thing to do is to write a letter. _____ you write one?

5 We have all agreed that we _____ boycott that large supermarket.

6 The council hasn't got enough money. They _____ close the pool. I hope they don't.

> I can express certainty and possibility.
> MY EVALUATION   ▢▢▢▢

READING ● The food waste scandal

3 Add *un-*, *im-* or *in-* to the words in the box. Then use them to complete the dialogues.

> sensitive   happy   acceptable   patient
> perfect   healthy

1 Do you eat _____ food like burgers? No, we always eat lots of salad.

2 What do supermarkets do with damaged or _____ vegetables? They just throw them away.

3 Hurry up! We need to go now. Wait a minute. Don't be so _____.

4 Why are you _____? My brother threw away the nice cake that I made. He's very _____.

5 What do you think about food waste? I think it's _____. The supermarkets should stop it.

> I can understand a text about food waste.
> MY EVALUATION   ▢▢▢▢

LANGUAGE FOCUS ● First conditional

4 Complete the sentences with the correct form of the verbs in brackets.

1 If we _____ (organize) a campaign, we _____ (save) part of the rainforest.

2 Freddie _____ (not come) on the march if it _____ (rain) on Saturday.

3 If I _____ (collect) some money, I _____ (give) it to the animal charity.

4 If Jake _____ (start) a campaign, we _____ (help) him.

5 You _____ (lose) your camera if you _____ (not put) it in your bag.

6 Emily _____ (not pass) the exam if she _____ (not study) hard.

> I can speculate about the future.
> MY EVALUATION   ▢▢▢▢

VOCABULARY AND LISTENING ● Phrasal verbs: a campaign

5 Complete the sentences with a phrasal verb. Use a synonym of the verb in brackets.

1 In the future, humans might _____ the birds in this forest. (destroy)
2 We want to _____ more information about this rare species. (discover)
3 I'm going on holiday to the Amazon. Can you _____ my pets? (care for)
4 My dad wants to _____ a new charity to save the rainforest. (start)
5 We're talking about animals in danger. You can _____ our discussion if you want. (participate in)
6 Will farmers _____ destroying the rainforest? Or will they stop? (continue)

> **I can understand an interview about rainforests.**
> MY EVALUATION ☐☐☐☐

LANGUAGE FOCUS ● *be going to* and *will*

6 Choose the correct words.

1 Why are you buying those art pencils? **I'll / I'm going to** draw a picture for my homework.
2 Have you broken her computer? I'm sure **she'll / she's going to** be very angry.
3 We talked to Joshua and Helen yesterday. **They'll / They're going to** move to France.
4 I'm very busy tonight. I don't think **I'll / I'm going to** watch TV.
5 Do you think **we'll / we're going to** collect enough money?
6 My father is on holiday this week. **He'll / He's going to** paint the house.

> **I can talk about the future.**
> MY EVALUATION ☐☐☐☐

SPEAKING ● Plans and arrangements

7 Put the dialogue in the correct order. Number the sentences.

a ☐ Ellie — Thanks very much, Mrs Quinn. Bye.
b ☐ Mrs Quinn — Hello, Ellie. What can I do for you?
c ☐ Mrs Quinn — Yes, of course. It sounds like a very good cause.
d ☐ Ellie — Hi, Mrs Quinn. Have you got a minute?
e ☐ Ellie — It's for a hospital charity. Will you come and buy a cake?
f ☐ Mrs Quinn — That's great! What's it for?
g ☐ Ellie — I'm organizing a cake sale tomorrow at school.

> **I can make plans and arrangements.**
> MY EVALUATION ☐☐☐☐

WRITING ● A formal letter

8 Complete the text with the words in the box.

> hand faithfully reason hope represent therefore If opinion concerned Madam

Dear Sir or ¹_____,

We ²_____ an organization called 'Save our Pool'. We are writing to you because we are ³_____ about plans to close the open-air swimming pool in our town. In our ⁴_____, the pool is very important to our area. ⁵_____ we close it, young people will have nothing to do. On the other ⁶_____, if we keep it open, we will have a wonderful place for the future.

We have ⁷_____ decided to take action and we are going to organize a campaign. For this ⁸_____, we are sending you some posters and leaflets to publicize 'Save our Pool'.
We ⁹_____ you will help to support us.

Yours ¹⁰_____

Charlotte Brown and Ryan Baker

> **I can write a formal letter.**
> MY EVALUATION ☐☐☐☐

7 ⬚⬚⬚⬚⬚⬚⬚⬚⬚ Film and fiction

VOCABULARY ● Books and films: genres

1 ⭐ Look at the photos. Complete the words.

a s _py_ f _ilm_

1 a d_____

2 a t_____

3 a f_____

4 a w_____

f_____

5 a m_____

6 a w_____

2 ⭐⭐ Complete the sentences with the words in the box.

> cartoon   comedies   detective stories
> thriller   science fiction   spy film   ~~westerns~~

They make a lot of ___westerns___ in Spain because it looks like the American Wild West.

1 I love _____. Jim Carrey really makes me laugh.

2 *The Bourne Identity* is a classic _____.

3 Isaac Asimov is one of the most famous _____ writers. He wrote *I, Robot*.

4 He likes old _____ like *Sherlock Holmes*.

5 *James Bond* is a great _____ series.

6 My favourite _____ is *The Simpsons*.

3 ⭐⭐ Match words 1–8 with definitions a–h.

1 an adventure story

2 a romance

3 a horror film

4 a science fiction story

5 a comedy

6 a musical

7 a mystery

8 a drama

a A story that makes you laugh a lot.

b A play or a story about people's lives, often in the past.

c An exciting novel with a fast-moving story.

d A scary film that makes people scream.

e A story that leaves you guessing until the end!

f A book about love and relationships.

g A story about space travel and visits to other planets.

h A film with singing and dancing.

4 ⭐⭐⭐ Answer the questions. Write complete sentences.

What's your favourite film genre? Why?

My favourite film genre is drama. I love history and
seeing old styles of clothes and houses.

1 What's your favourite film genre? Why?

_____

2 What's your favourite book genre? Why?

_____

3 What book are you reading at the moment? What genre is it?

_____

4 What films have you watched recently? What genres were they?

_____

5 What film genres do you never watch? Why not?

_____

6 What book genres do you never read? Why not?

_____

Verbs + -ing / to

1 ★ Choose the correct words.

My mum doesn't like **to shop** /(shopping.)

1 Would you like **watching** / **to watch** this film?
2 We love **to eat** / **eating** in Chinese restaurants.
3 I'd prefer **riding** / **to ride** your bicycle.
4 Does she like **to appear** / **appearing** on TV?
5 We wouldn't like **having** / **to have** tests every day.
6 She's finished **to read** / **reading** your novel.
7 They've decided **to go** / **going** home.
8 I don't need **to record** / **recording** this film.

2 ★★ Write questions using the -ing or to form of the verbs in bold. Then write true answers.

do / you / like / **shop**

<u>Do you like shopping?</u>

<u>No, I hate shopping. It's boring!</u>

1 do / you / mind / **wash up**

_____
_____

2 do / you / prefer / **play** / football or tennis

_____
_____

3 do / you / need / **do** / homework tonight

_____
_____

4 does / your best friend / prefer / **talk** / or / listen

_____
_____

5 do / you / enjoy / **watch** / horror films

_____
_____

6 have / you / finished / **do** / this exercise

_____
_____

7 would / you / like / **read** / a comic

_____
_____

could, can, will be able to

3 ★★ Look at the table. Complete the sentences with *could*, *couldn't*, *can*, *can't* or *will be able to*.

name age now	swim	speak English	drive
Pam: age 15	6 years old	12 years old	one day
Kate: age 16	9 years old	15 years old	one day
Simon: age 21	12 years old	one day	17 years old

Pam ___can___ swim. Pam ___could___ swim when she was six.

1 Pam _____ swim when she was five.
2 Kate and Simon _____ swim.
3 Kate _____ swim when she was nine.
4 Kate and Pam _____ drive now.
5 Kate and Pam _____ drive one day.
6 Simon _____ drive.
7 Kate _____ speak English when she was ten.
8 Kate _____ speak English now.
9 Simon _____ speak English now.
10 Simon _____ speak English one day.

4 ★★★ Complete the table about you and a person in your family. Then write eight sentences using the correct forms of *could, can* and *will be able to*.

name	speak English	swim	drive	ride a bicycle
me	12 years old	_____	_____	_____
	_____	_____	_____	_____

<u>I could speak English when I was twelve.</u>

1 _____
2 _____
3 _____
4 _____
5 _____
6 _____
7 _____
8 _____

VOCABULARY ● Books and films: features

1 ⭐ Match sentence halves 1–7 with a–g.

1 My favourite novelist is
2 I've read a biography
3 Computers can create
4 I think the best science fiction film director is
5 One of the film's cast
6 The theme was
7 Blockbusters are films

a Steven Spielberg. He made *ET*.
b great special effects.
c Philip Pullman, who wrote *Northern Lights*.
d the importance of families.
e which make a lot of money.
f about the life of Michael Jackson.
g is a famous actor.

2 ⭐⭐ Choose the correct answers.

The words of a film written on the screen in another language are _____.
(**a** subtitles) **b** special effects **c** scripts

1 A person who writes books is a _____.
 a publisher **b** novelist **c** film director
2 The first page of a story is the _____.
 a setting **b** theme **c** beginning
3 The last minute of a film is the _____.
 a special effects **b** ending **c** scene
4 The _____ of a book or a film could be, for example, crime, love or honesty.
 a setting **b** theme **c** scene
5 Computer-generated images for films are _____.
 a special effects **b** subtitles **c** plots
6 A _____ is a book that is very popular.
 a best-seller **b** script **c** special effects
7 The _____ is the story in a book or a film.
 a cast **b** character **c** plot
8 A _____ is the story of somebody's life.
 a script **b** publisher **c** biography

3 ⭐⭐ Complete the text with the words in the box.

> character director plot scenes
> setting ~~special-effects~~ themes

DVD review

I liked *Thor* and *Green Lantern*, but my favourite film is still *Spider-Man 3*. It's got some amazing _special effects_ and the ¹_____ with Venom and the Sandman are brilliant. As with the first two Spider-Man films, the ²_____ is New York City. Tobey Maguire plays the main ³_____, Peter Parker (Spider-Man), and the ⁴_____ of the film is Sam Raimi. The ⁵_____ are love, and the fight of good against bad. The ⁶_____ is fast-moving, so it's never boring.

4 ⭐⭐⭐ Answer the questions. Write complete sentences.

Which novelists do you like? What have they written?
I like Stephenie Meyer. She wrote the Twilight books.

1 Do you prefer reading best-sellers or books that aren't famous? Why?
_____

2 Do you prefer books or films with a happy ending, or a sad ending? Give an example.
_____

3 Who's your favourite character from a book or a film? Why do you like this character?
_____

4 What are the best special effects you've seen in a film?
_____

5 What do you think of films with subtitles?
_____

1 ⭐ Look at the table. Choose the correct words.

Situation	Result
If I watched a horror film,	I'd be / 'll be scared.
If you ¹didn't know / 'd know,	you wouldn't be annoyed.
If he ²have / had lots of money,	would he buy a boat?

Result	Situation
They'd ³got / get good marks	if they revised.
She wouldn't mind	if you ⁴stayed / wouldn't stay up late.
Where would you go	if we ⁵wouldn't be / weren't at school?

2 ⭐⭐ Order the words to make sentences and questions. There is one word or phrase that you do not need.

watch / the western if / we'd / wasn't on. / ~~watched~~ / this thriller
<u>We'd watch the western if this thriller wasn't on.</u>

1 she / doesn't / wouldn't / read novels if / she / didn't / like them.
_____
_____

2 would / we / went / we see if / what / to the cinema? / will go
_____
_____

3 would send / he'd / be / him this email. / angry if you / sent
_____
_____

4 have / I'd blog about / had / a computer. / the film if I
_____
_____

5 wouldn't / I'll / I didn't / I / study hard. / get good marks if
_____
_____

6 she / we / asked her? / would / be in the cast if / was in the cast if
_____
_____

3 ⭐⭐ Complete the sentences using the second conditional.

If you ___painted___ (paint) your bedroom, what colour ___would___ you ___choose___? (choose)

1 We _____ (not queue) for three hours if we _____ (not want) to see the film.

2 If they _____ (enjoy) *Spider-Man 3*, they _____ (love) *Thor*.

3 _____ you _____ (tell) Mum if I _____ (come) home late?

4 She _____ (not expel) you if you _____ (apologize).

5 I _____ (fall) asleep if I _____ (watch) another musical!

6 _____ you _____ (help) your friend if he _____ (be) in trouble?

4 ⭐⭐⭐ Write questions using the second conditional. Then write true answers.

you / complain / if / somebody / copy / your essay
<u>Would you complain if somebody copied your essay?</u>
<u>Yes, I'd tell the teacher if somebody copied my essay.</u>

1 what / you / buy / if / you / have / £1,000
_____
_____

2 if / you / be / a professional footballer, / who / you / play / for
_____
_____

3 if / you / be / the president, / what / you / ban
_____
_____

4 what / you / do / if / your phone / ring in the cinema
_____
_____

5 if / you / watch / only one film this month, / what / you / choose
_____
_____

6 who / you / call / if / you / have / only one minute of credit on your phone
_____
_____

1 ⭐ Read the text. Tick ✓ the correct box.

The author wrote the text to …

a ☐ report some news.
b ☐ complain about something.
c ☐ inform the reader.

The digital revolution and you

Books first appeared 2,000 years ago. People wrote by hand, so no two books looked the same. Books were big, heavy and expensive and not many people could read.

The first revolution was Gutenberg's invention of the printing press in 1440. Printing presses could print thousands of books quickly and cheaply. By 1500 there were 20 million books in Europe and millions of people learnt to read. Today, 99% of Europeans can read.

The second revolution was more recent. Publishers started to use computers to produce books about twenty years ago. Traditional presses started to disappear and people began to produce books electronically. People also started to read newspapers and magazines online and some people thought that paper books would disappear one day.

Now the digital revolution is here! E-book readers have arrived and personal webpages and blogs have also become more popular. Did you know that 31% of people between the ages of fourteen and twenty-one have got their own blog or webpage?

'Print on demand' is another part of the digital revolution. Soon, you'll be able to choose a book from a selection of millions in any bookshop. A machine will print your book while you wait in the shop! You'll be able to print books that you've written, too.

2 ⭐⭐ Read the text again. Choose the correct answers.

_____ could read 2,000 years ago.

a Nearly everybody (**b** Only a few people)
c Nobody

1 _____ could produce a lot of books cheaply.
   a Handwriting   **b** Printing presses
   c Webpages
2 Publishers have produced _____ for 20 years.
   a e-books   **b** computers
   c books using computers
3 A lot of people aged 14–21 have got _____.
   a webpages and blogs
   b e-books
   c newspapers and magazines
4 Soon, you will be able to print _____ with 'print on demand'.
   a your own book   **b** an e-book   **c** a website

3 ⭐⭐⭐ Answer the questions. Write complete sentences.

Why did books look different 2,000 years ago?
<u>They looked different because people wrote each</u>
<u>one by hand.</u>

1 How does the writer describe the books of 2,000 years ago?
   _____
   _____

2 What were the advantages of printing presses?
   _____
   _____

3 Why did some people think that books would disappear?
   _____
   _____

4 What is 'print on demand'?
   _____
   _____

Build your vocabulary

4 ⭐⭐ Complete the text with suffixes *-er(s)* or *-or(s)*.

My uncle's a film direct **or** and I went to the first night of his new film on Friday. There were three ¹speak___: my uncle, the ²produc___ and two of the ³act___.

The film was in French with subtitles, so the ⁴translat___ came to talk about his work on the translation.

After the speeches, they started the film, but the ⁵project___ broke! Luckily, there was an orchestra to play music at the party after the film. The ⁶conduct___ realized the problem, and asked the orchestra to start playing immediately.

Language point: Paragraphs and topic sentences

1 ⭐ Read the text and order the paragraphs.

1 [B] Introduction (facts)
2 ☐ Setting and characters (facts)
3 ☐ Theme and plot (opinion)
4 ☐ Conclusion (opinion)

2 ⭐⭐ Match sentences 1–4 with paragraphs A–D.

1 Christopher becomes a detective. ___
2 A great book for everyone! ___
3 Christopher is clever. ___
4 The author has won several awards for the novel. ___

A I particularly enjoyed the themes of loss and love in the novel. It's a mystery story and the plot is about Christopher looking for answers, after he finds his neighbour's dog dead in the garden. The thing I liked most about the book was how it's serious, but funny at the same time.

B I'd like to recommend *The Curious Incident of the Dog in the Night-Time*. It was the first best-seller by the award-winning novelist Mark Haddon.

C All in all, it's a brilliant book. I wouldn't change it. I think anyone would enjoy it, not just children.

D The setting is Swindon and London, in the south of England, and the main character is a boy called Christopher. He's fifteen and he's very good at maths, but he can't make friends easily, because he is autistic.

☐ TASK

3 ⭐⭐ Read the notes about the film and complete the review.

Recent film: 'Friends Forever?' (drama)
Setting: Preston, England
Main characters: Daisy Jennings, Layla Evans
DETAILS:
1 Daisy: move to Preston
2 Layla: become Daisy's friend
3 Layla: very popular
4 Layla: start to bully Daisy
5 Daisy: feel very sad
Film: very realistic – how relationships change
OPINION:
Really like the story
Ending not happy, but anyone enjoy it

I'd like to recommend a film that I watched ___**recently**___ called ¹_____.
The film is a ²_____ and the ³_____ is Preston, England. The main ⁴_____.
In the film, Daisy moves ⁵_____ and Layla ⁶_____ her friend. ⁷_____ popular at school. Soon, Layla starts to ⁸_____ Daisy. Daisy ⁹_____ very sad.
The thing I liked most about the film is that ¹⁰_____ because it shows ¹¹_____.
All in all, I ¹²_____. The ending ¹³_____, but I think anyone ¹⁴_____.

4 ⭐⭐⭐ Write a review of a TV programme which you have enjoyed. Use the text in exercise 3 to help you.

MY EVALUATION   Check your progress. Do the exercises and then complete your own evaluation.

▣☐☐☐ I need to try this again.   ▣▣▣☐ I am happy with this.

▣▣☐☐ I could do this better.   ▣▣▣▣ I can do this very well.

VOCABULARY AND LANGUAGE FOCUS ●
Books and films: genres

1 Complete the sentences.

1 Would you like to read a _____? (love story)

2 I don't like _____. (stories with robots and spaceships)

3 I hated that _____! Were you frightened, too? (very scary film)

4 Would you like to watch a _____? (film with a lot of singing and dancing)

5 I hate _____. (films with soldiers and fighting)

6 It was a really funny _____. (film that makes you laugh)

7 Do you like _____? (films made with moving drawings or pictures)

8 I'd prefer to watch a _____. (cowboy film)

2 Complete the sentences using the correct form of the verbs in brackets.

1 I'd like _____ (meet) Mia Wasikowska.

2 I'd like _____ (borrow) this DVD.

3 I don't like _____ (cook).

4 Do they prefer _____ (walk) or _____ (cycle)?

5 We'd prefer _____ (go) skiing.

6 My sister loves _____ (sing) in the shower.

7 I'd like _____ (watch) a horror film later.

8 I don't mind _____ (read) at home.

I can talk about likes and dislikes.

MY EVALUATION ☐☐☐☐

READING ● Movie technology

3 Complete the text with the suffixes -*or*, -*ors* or -*ers*.

The first film [1]act___ didn't need to speak because films didn't have sound. Instead, there was a pianist or sometimes an orchestra and [2]conduct___ in the cinema to accompany the film. In the 1930s, film [3]produc___ introduced music and then speaking into their films. By the 1960s, [4]view___ were watching colour films. In recent years, the sound and picture quality in films has improved with the invention of the digital [5]project___.

I can understand a text about the history of cinema.

MY EVALUATION ☐☐☐☐

LANGUAGE FOCUS ● *could, can, will be able to*

4 Complete the sentences using the correct form of *could*, *can* or *will be able to*.

1 My parents _____ speak English really well. They learnt it at school.

2 I _____ ride a bike when I was ten. I learnt when I was on holiday when I was eight.

3 My brother _____ drive last year. He's learning now.

4 I think I _____ get a good job when I leave school.

5 I _____ swim now, but I'm not very good.

6 My best friend is clever. I think he _____ go to university one day.

7 _____ you ride a bike when you were five?

I can talk about ability and possibility.

MY EVALUATION ☐☐☐☐

VOCABULARY AND LISTENING ● Books and films: features

5 Complete the dialogue.

Baz What kind of books do you like?
Sue I like to read ¹b _ _ _-s _ _ _ _ _ _, like *Twilight*.
Baz I prefer science fiction and horror stories because they usually have an exciting ²p _ _ _ and they're often in unusual ³s _ _ _ _ _ _s.
Sue Who is your favourite ⁴n _ _ _ _ _ _?
Baz Stephen King, definitely.
Sue What do you think of the films of Stephen King's novels?
Baz Films like *The Mist* are brilliant, but Stephen King doesn't write the film ⁵s _ _ _ _ _ _. He only writes novels.
Sue How do you know all this?
Baz I've read his ⁶b _ _ _ _ _ _ _ _ on his webpage.

> **I can understand a programme about books and films.**
> MY EVALUATION ☐☐☐☐

LANGUAGE FOCUS ● Second conditional

6 Write second conditional sentences.

1 be / rich / I / become / a pilot
If I _____.

2 I / fly / you to Hollywood / I / be / a pilot
_____

3 be / in Hollywood / we / visit / Universal Studios
If we _____

4 meet / Brad Pitt / he / put / us in a movie
If we _____

5 we / become / famous / we / be / in the cast of a Hollywood movie
_____

6 be / rich / you / buy / a plane / ?
If you _____

> **I can talk about imaginary situations.**
> MY EVALUATION ☐☐☐☐

SPEAKING ● Expressing preferences and recommending

7 Complete the dialogue with the words in the box.

> about this one   don't fancy   might like
> not a big fan of   recommend that   this one

Fiona Would you like to watch a war film?
Shaun No, I'm ¹_____ war films.
Fiona Well, try ²_____. *The Adventures of Tintin*. The director's Steven Spielberg.
Shaun I've seen that.
Fiona What ³_____?
Shaun I've seen that, too.
Fiona If we had *Monster House*, I'd ⁴_____. Ah, you ⁵_____ this one.
Shaun No, I ⁶_____ that either. Sorry!

> **I can talk about books and films that I prefer.**
> MY EVALUATION ☐☐☐☐

WRITING ● A review of a book or a film

8 Choose the correct answers to complete the book review.

Claimed by Shadows

I have recently ¹_____ *Claimed by Shadows*, by the American novelist Karen Chance.
I'd ²_____ this book to anyone who enjoyed the *Twilight* series. The ³_____ is Las Vegas and the main ⁴_____ is Cassie, an American teenager.
The theme is about being brave. I ⁵_____ enjoyed the plot, which is about some vampires who are trying to catch Cassie. The best bit was when she travels through time from modern America to London in the 1870s.
All in ⁶_____, I really enjoyed it.

1 a read   b changed   c recommended
2 a like   b recommend   c enjoy
3 a plot   b theme   c setting
4 a character   b scene   c setting
5 a very   b particularly   c recently
6 a all   b recently   c end

> **I can write a book or a film review.**
> MY EVALUATION ☐☐☐☐

VOCABULARY ● Nouns: art

1 ⭐ Label the photos with the words in the box.

> sculpture   landscape   museum
> ~~gallery~~   auction   painting

gallery

1 _____

2 _____

3 _____

4 _____

5 _____

2 ⭐⭐ Choose the correct answers.

The artist painted a new _____ of the president.

a masterpiece   b landscape   [c portrait]

1 The _____ wrote articles about the exhibition in the newspapers.
   a landscapes   b masterpieces   c critics

2 We went to a big _____ to watch the collectors buy and sell paintings.
   a exhibition   b auction   c museum

3 That beautiful painting sold for £50,000,000. It's a real _____.
   a masterpiece   b collector   c landscape

4 My uncle is an art _____. He buys a lot of paintings every year.
   a critic   b auction   c collector

5 The students studied some of the painters from the Cubist _____.
   a art movement   b portrait   c masterpiece

6 That artist has got a new _____ at a big gallery in London.
   a museum   b critic   c exhibition

3 ⭐⭐ Complete the dialogue with the words in the box.

> exhibition   ~~critic~~   collector   gallery
> portrait   sculptures   masterpiece

Karl The ___critic___ in the newspaper says this painting is terrible. What do you think?

Emma I don't agree with him at all. I think it's a ¹_____!

Karl What did you think of that ²_____ of paintings at the new art ³_____ in town?

Emma It was OK. But I didn't like the ⁴_____ of Angelina Jolie. It didn't look like her at all.

Karl If you were an art ⁵_____, what sort of things would you buy?

Emma I think I'd get a lot of big ⁶_____ for my garden.

4 ⭐⭐⭐ Complete the letter with words in exercises 1–3.

> Hi, Alex!
> You wanted to know about what art to see when you come to London. Here are some suggestions.
>   There are a lot of wonderful __galleries__ to visit in London. One of the most famous is Tate Britain. You can see many different types of ¹_____ by famous artists here. There are ²_____ of kings and queens. There are also beautiful ³_____ which show the hills, trees and rivers of the British countryside.
>   If you want to watch people buy and sell art, you can also go to an ⁴_____.
> A lot of international art ⁵_____ come to buy paintings.
>   If you're interested in things from ancient Egypt or Rome, then go to the British ⁶_____. You can see old coins, statues and jewellery.
> Write soon
> Amy

Present passive: affirmative and negative

1 (★) **Complete the table with the words in the box.**

> 'm̶   paid   isn't   're   aren't   's
> influenced   'm not

Affirmative
I <u>'m</u> influenced by the Dada movement.
He / She / It ¹_____ influenced by the Dada movement.
You / We / You / They ²_____ ³_____ by the Dada movement.

Negative
I ⁴_____ paid by the museum.
He / She / It ⁵_____ paid by the museum.
You / We / You / They ⁶_____ ⁷_____ by the museum.

2 (★★) **Complete the text using the passive form of the verb in brackets.**

BANKSY

Banksy's art is very famous and he <u>is known</u> (know) all over the world, but nobody is sure who he is or what his real name is. He ¹_____ (not call) 'Banksy' in real life.

Banksy's graffiti art ²_____ (talk) about a lot on TV and radio. His works ³_____ (study) by a lot of art students, too. However, Banksy isn't popular with everybody. His works ⁴_____ (reject) by some traditional art collectors and critics.

If you go to London, you can see a lot of Banksy's works. Of course, his pictures ⁵_____ (not find) in traditional art galleries, they ⁶_____ (paint) on lots of walls around the city.

Past passive: affirmative and negative

3 (★★) **Rewrite each sentence in the passive. Start each sentence with the words in bold.**

They built **the new art gallery** in 2009.
<u>The new art gallery was built in 2009.</u>

1 Somebody found **the pictures** in an old house.
_____

2 Naomi and Simon won **the first prize**.
_____

3 The police didn't catch **the art thief**.
_____

4 They didn't sell **the portraits** yesterday.
_____

5 Somebody took **that big sculpture** on Friday.
_____

6 Pablo Picasso painted **these masterpieces**.
_____

7 A famous artist opened **the exhibition**.
_____

4 (★★★) **Rewrite the text using the passive when possible.**

The Scream

The Scream is one of the world's most famous images. The Norwegian artist Edvard Munch painted it. He produced several versions of the painting.

In 2004, someone stole one version of the painting. Fortunately, someone photographed the thieves and in the end, the police found the painting.

The Scream

<u>The Scream is one of the world's most famous images. It</u>
<u>was painted by the Norwegian artist Edvard Munch.</u>
_____
_____
_____
_____
_____
_____
_____
_____
_____

1 ⭐ **Complete the words in the sentences.**

This artist is very different from other artists.
He's very o **r i g i n a l** .

1 I thought that exhibition was really
   d _ _ _ and boring.
2 Her sculptures are very original and
   i _ _ _ _ _ _ _ _ _ .
3 The woman in the painting had long dark
   hair. She was very b _ _ _ _ _ _ _ .
4 The masterpiece is very c _ _ _ _ _ _ _ _ .
   The artist used green, yellow, blue, red and
   orange.
5 Some painters make people upset or angry
   with their p _ _ _ _ _ _ _ _ _ pictures.
6 The critics couldn't agree on the new portrait.
   It was very c _ _ _ _ _ _ _ _ _ _ _ .
7 His style of painting comes from the
   eighteenth century. It's very
   t _ _ _ _ _ _ _ _ _ .
8 We all laughed at the portrait. It was
   incredibly a _ _ _ _ _ _ .
9 I don't really like that unusual sculpture made
   from rubbish. It's a bit s _ _ _ _ _ _ .

2 ⭐⭐ **Match the adjectives 1–7 with the reviews a–g.**

1 colourful   **b**
2 dull   _____
3 shocking   _____
4 ridiculous   _____
5 amusing   _____
6 original   _____
7 controversial _____

a This latest exhibition isn't very interesting at all.

b There isn't a boring black and white painting anywhere in the gallery!

c We've never seen art like this anywhere before. It's completely new!

d I thought this artist's cartoons were funny.

e Nobody can agree on these new paintings. Everybody is talking about them.

f The new portrait of the president was particularly silly and stupid.

g This painter's work made me feel really angry and surprised.

3 ⭐⭐ **Complete the sentences with the words in the box.**

> shocking   imaginative   traditional
> beautiful   strange   ~~provocative~~
> colourful

I think that artist is very _**provocative**_. She always shocks people.

1 Do you like that black and white painting?
   No, it isn't _____ enough.
2 The building was designed in a Roman style.
   It isn't modern. It's very _____.
3 These sculptures are very nice to look at.
   They're really _____.
4 She thought that the exhibition was a bit
   _____ because there were only two
   pictures.
5 Do you like painting?
   Yes, but I'm not very _____. I can't
   think of creative ideas.
6 We couldn't look at the photographs of the
   war for long. They were too _____.

4 ⭐⭐⭐ **Complete the sentences using your own ideas. Say why you like or don't like the different things.**

A CD cover that I like is '**Dig out your Soul**' by
Oasis because it's imaginative and original.

1 A DVD cover that I like is _____
   because _____.
2 A book cover that I like is _____
   because _____.
3 A painting that I don't like is _____
   because _____.
4 A poster that I like is _____
   because _____.
5 A building that I don't like is _____
   because _____.

1 ⭐ **Complete the table with the words in the box.**

> ~~was~~ given were was was were
> wasn't was painted weren't wasn't
> frightened

Affirmative
I ___was___ painted by the artist.
He / She / It ¹_____ painted by the artist.
You / We / They ²_____ ³_____ by the artist.

Negative
I ⁴_____ given any food at the gallery.
He / She / It ⁵_____ given any food at the gallery.
You / We / They ⁶_____ ⁷_____ any food at the gallery.

Questions
⁸_____ I frightened by the strange picture?
⁹_____ he / she / it frightened by the strange picture?
¹⁰_____ you / we / they ¹¹_____ by the strange picture?

2 ⭐⭐ **Complete the sentences using the present or past passive form of the verbs in brackets.**

These paintings __were bought__ (buy) by an American collector.

1 Bananas _____ (grow) in hot countries.
2 These pictures _____ (not paint) by the artist Rembrandt.
3 _____ this modern chair _____ (make) of plastic?
4 The film *Titanic* _____ (not direct) by Steven Spielberg.
5 Tigers _____ (not find) in Africa.
6 When _____ the Eiffel Tower _____ (build)?
7 This is an old song. It _____ (sing) by the *Spice Girls* in 1996.
8 The Harry Potter characters _____ (create) by J.K. Rowling.

3 ⭐⭐ **Write questions for this quiz using the present or past passive. Then match questions 1–6 with answers a–g.**

General Knowledge Quiz

when / Olympic Games / hold / in Beijing
__When were the Olympic Games held in Beijing?__ __a__

1 when / printing / press / invent
_____ ___

2 where / tea and coffee / grow
_____ ___

3 where / Museum of Picasso / build
_____ ___

4 who / *The Persistence of Memory* / paint / by
_____ ___

5 when / *Mona Lisa* / paint
_____ ___

6 when / American Independence Day / celebrate
_____ ___

a 2008   e 1440
b 16th century   f 4th July
c Salvador Dalí   g Spain
d Africa

4 ⭐⭐⭐ **Complete the questions using the present or past passive. Then look at the notes and answer them.**

Famous visitor attractions	
Name	The London Eye
Location	Central London, next to River Thames
Architects	David Marks and Julia Barfield
Completed	1999
Opened	31st December 1999 by Tony Blair

What __is it called__? (call)
__It's called the London Eye.__

1 Where _____? (locate)
_____

2 Who _____? (design by)
_____

3 When _____? (finish)
_____

4 When _____? (open)
_____

5 Who _____? (open by)
_____

Disaster at Museum!

A The Fitzwilliam Museum in Cambridge was founded in 1816 and has a large number of world-famous paintings and fine ceramics. Wednesday 25th January 2006 was another ordinary day in the museum. Visitors were walking quietly around the galleries and looking at the museum's collection of masterpieces.

B Suddenly, the staff heard a very loud noise and they ran to the museum's staircase. At the bottom of the stairs, they found a man who was surrounded by broken vases.

C The staff soon learnt the whole story. The visitor, Nick Flynn, was tying his shoelaces when he fell down the stairs. He hit a large jar and two vases which were standing on a big windowsill next to the staircase. They immediately fell over and broke into hundreds of pieces.

D The jar and the vases are extremely valuable and were given to the museum by Anthony de Rothschild in 1948. They were made in China in the late seventeenth century and are very large. The jar is eighty centimetres high and weighs around forty-five kilograms. Two people are needed to carry it.

E Fortunately, the story has a happy ending. Nick Flynn was unhurt and the museum accepted that it was an accident. The jar and the two vases were carefully restored. It took seven months to put them back together. They are now on display again at the museum – but this time they are in strong glass cases.

1 ⭐ **Read the text. Tick ✓ the correct box.**

The author wrote the text to …

a ☐ describe a masterpiece.
b ☐ make a complaint.
c ☐ tell a story.

2 ⭐⭐ **Read the text again. Match topics 1–5 with paragraphs A–E.**

1 A fall which ended in disaster. <u>C</u>
2 The vases return. ___
3 The staff arrive quickly. ___
4 A quiet day at the Fitzwilliam. ___
5 Huge vases with a long history. ___

3 ⭐⭐ **Find the words in the text and match them with definitions a–f.**

1 founded
2 ordinary
3 staff
4 shoelace
5 windowsill
6 restored

a a string that you use to fasten a shoe
b normal; not unusual
c started; set up
d a shelf under a window
e people who work in an organization
f made as good as before

4 ⭐⭐⭐ **Answer the questions. Write complete sentences.**

1 When did the accident happen?
_____

2 Why did the staff run to the staircase?
_____

3 What was Nick Flynn doing when the accident happened?
_____

4 How many things did Nick Flynn break?
_____

5 Where were the jar and vases made?
_____

6 What happened to the vases in the end?
_____

Build your vocabulary

5 ⭐⭐ **Choose the correct synonym for the words in bold.**

We **love** his new painting. (dislike, adore, hate)

1 He's a very **important** politician. (influential, famous, attractive)
2 What are the **aims** of your plan? (characteristics, objectives, ideas)
3 The sculpture exhibition was **excellent**. (exceptional, exciting, exclusive)
4 It's a very **strange** work of art. (everyday, usual, unusual)
5 The instructions for our homework were quite **clear**. (straightforward, unusual, common)

Language point: Using synonyms

1 ⭐ Are the words in brackets synonyms for the words in bold? Write ✓ or ✗.

The man in the portrait was very **handsome**. (good-looking) _____✓_____

1 The modern art museum in New York is very **large**.
(big) _____

2 They decided to **close** the museum at five o'clock.
(shut) _____

3 Examples of the artist's work are very **rare**.
(common) _____

4 I can't find the **answer** to this problem.
(question) _____

5 She's **frightened** of big dogs.
(afraid) _____

6 There was a **massive** sculpture outside the art gallery.
(tiny) _____

2 ⭐⭐ Match the synonyms in the box with the words in bold in the text.

> gave back ~~yearly~~ a fortnight clever
> pupil frequently errors close to
> annoyed stupid

We had our **annual** maths exam at school **¹two weeks** ago. When my teacher **²returned** my exam paper, I felt a bit **³angry** with myself. I knew most of the answers, but there were a lot of **⁴silly ⁵mistakes**.

My teacher **⁶often** says that I'm a very **⁷intelligent ⁸student**, but I need to listen more in class! It's true - I usually sit **⁹near** the window and sometimes look outside.

_____yearly_____   5 _____
1 _____   6 _____
2 _____   7 _____
3 _____   8 _____
4 _____   9 _____

☐ TASK

3 ⭐⭐ Read the notes and complete the text.

Paragraph 1

it / paint/ by my grandfather

it / give to me / a few years ago

Paragraph 2

they / make / from blue glass

they / produce / in the south of Italy

they / bring back / from holiday / by a friend / last year

Paragraph 3

they /send / to /me / by my family and school friends

some of them / write / a long time ago

My favourite things

In my bedroom, I've got a little collection of my favourite things. On the wall, there's a small portrait of my mum when she was four. It was **painted by my grandfather** and ¹_____
_____.

On the table near my bed, there are two small bowls – ²_____
_____.
I think ³_____
_____, but I'm not sure. ⁴_____
_____
I usually put all my pens and pencils in them.

The best things in my room are the postcards. I've got hundreds of them.
⁵_____
_____.
Some of them ⁶_____
_____. But I still keep them above my bed and I look at them every night.

The Prophet's Mosque Madinah

The Holy Mosque, Makkah

4 ⭐⭐⭐ Write about three of your favourite things. Use the text in exercise 3 to help you.

MY EVALUATION   Check your progress. Do the exercises and then complete your own evaluation.

☐☐☐☐ I need to try this again.   ☐☐☐☐ I am happy with this.

☐☐☐☐ I could do this better.   ☐☐☐☐ I can do this very well.

VOCABULARY AND LANGUAGE FOCUS ●
Nouns: art

1 Complete the dialogues with the words in the box.

> collector   exhibition   sculpture
> painting   art movement   auction

Mark   What did you buy at the
¹_____ today?

Rashid   A small ²_____. It's made of
stone.

Megan   Do you want to become an art
³_____ when you're older?

Josh   Yes, but I only have one ⁴_____
on my wall at the moment. It's called
River View.

Lewis   Did you like the new ⁵_____ at
the museum?

Jane   Yes, there were a lot of pictures from
the Cubist ⁶_____.

2 Complete the second sentence using the
passive, so that it has the same meaning as the
first sentence.

1 Collectors buy these paintings.
These paintings _____
_____

2 Some people paint graffiti in unusual places.
Graffiti _____.

3 They don't make these sculptures in Europe.
These sculptures _____
_____

4 A lot of people enjoy Banksy's work.
Banksy's work _____

5 Thousands of students visit the gallery every
year.
The gallery _____
_____

6 Some critics don't accept graffiti art.
Graffiti art _____

> **I can talk about artists and works of art.**
>
> MY EVALUATION   ☐☐☐☐

READING ● Dada

3 Replace the words in bold with the synonyms
from the box.

> adore   objective   unusual   influential
> intelligent   everyday

1 Some Dada art was quite **strange**. _____
2 I **love** that work by Marcel Duchamp.
_____
3 Modern artists often use **common** objects.
_____
4 Duchamp was a very **important** artist.
_____
5 A lot of Duchamp's work was **clever** and
amusing. _____
6 The main **aim** of the exhibition is to teach
people about Dada art. _____

> **I can understand a text about Dada art.**
>
> MY EVALUATION   ☐☐☐☐

LANGUAGE FOCUS ● Past passive:
affirmative and negative

4 Complete the sentences using the past passive
of the verbs in the box.

> not find   steal   build   break
> not paint   clean

1 The masterpieces _____ by criminals.
2 That famous art gallery _____ in 1574
and it's still open today.
3 The sculptures _____ by a small child.
4 The portrait _____ carefully because it
was very valuable.
5 These paintings _____ by the artist
Matisse. He didn't usually do landscapes.
6 The painting _____ by the police.

> **I can use the past passive to talk about art.**
>
> MY EVALUATION   ☐☐☐☐

VOCABULARY AND LISTENING ● Adjectives: describing art

5 Complete the words in the sentences.

1 We all laughed when we saw the picture. It was very a _ _ _ _ _ _.
2 That new exhibition was d_ _ _ and boring.
3 They loved the sculpture in yellow, blue and green. It was really c _ _ _ _ _ _ _ _.
4 I only like modern art. These paintings are too t _ _ _ _ _ _ _ _ _ for me.
5 We've never seen a portrait like this before. It's completely o _ _ _ _ _ _ _.
6 She couldn't look at the old war photographs for very long. They were very s _ _ _ _ _ _ _.
7 He's a really creative artist. He always paints i _ _ _ _ _ _ _ _ _ _ pictures.

> **I can describe art.**
> MY EVALUATION ☐☐☐☐

LANGUAGE FOCUS ● Present and past passive: affirmative, negative and questions

6 Complete the sentences using the present or past passive of the verb in brackets.

1 The museum _____ (visit) by a lot of people every day.
2 _____ those beautiful chairs _____ (make) of wood? Yes, they are.
3 Lemons _____ (not grow) in our country.
4 That sculpture _____ (create) by an Italian artist in 1523.
5 The famous portraits _____ (give) to a museum last year.
6 When _____ this art gallery _____ (open)?
7 Dada art _____ (not understand) by society at that time.

> **I can ask and answer quiz questions using the passive.**
> MY EVALUATION ☐☐☐☐

SPEAKING ● Expressing doubt

7 Choose the correct answers.

1 What do you think _____ this painting?
   a on b off c of d in
2 It _____ me of a picture by Cézanne.
   a minds b reminds c keeps d remembers
3 I'm not sure _____ that man in the picture.
   a to b on c by d about
4 He doesn't _____ like a person from Paris to me.
   a look b appear c show d represent
5 What _____ earth is that thing in the corner?
   a in b on c of d at
6 I think it looks _____ a child painted it.
   a if b as c as if d liked

> **I can express opinions and doubts.**
> MY EVALUATION ☐☐☐☐

WRITING ● A description of a piece of art

8 Put sentences a–d in the correct place in the text.

Café Terrace at Night was painted by Vincent van Gogh in September 1888. ¹_____. The scenery includes a café with tables and chairs in the foreground and a dark blue sky with stars in the background. ²_____.

This type of work is typical of post-impressionism, an art movement which started in France in the 1880s. ³_____.

Café Terrace at Night was first exhibited in 1892. It was bought by a Dutch art collector called Helene Kröller-Müller. ⁴_____. You can see it there today.

a It included other famous artists like Paul Cézanne and Henri Matisse.
b It is an oil painting and it shows a French street scene at night.
c It was later donated to a famous art museum in the Netherlands.
d It is said that this is Van Gogh's first painting with stars in a night sky.

> **I can write about a piece of art.**
> MY EVALUATION ☐☐☐☐

Comparative and superlative adjectives

To form comparative and superlative adjectives:

1 With one-syllable adjectives, add -er or the + -est.
   weak — weaker — the weakest
2 With adjectives that end in -e, add -r or the + -st.
   rare — rarer — the rarest
3 With adjectives that end in one vowel + one consonant, double the consonant and add -er or the + -est.
   big — bigger — the biggest
4 With adjectives that end in -y, remove the -y and add -ier or the + -iest.
   healthy — healthier — the healthiest
5 With adjectives of two or more syllables, put more or the most before the adjective.
   dangerous — more dangerous — the most dangerous

Remember: some adjectives are irregular.

good — better — the best   bad — worse — the worst

Use

We use comparative adjectives + than to compare two or more things or people.

London is bigger than Oxford.   You're taller than me.

We use superlative adjectives to compare a thing or a person with the whole group he / she / it belongs to.

Everest is the tallest mountain in the world.

Present simple

Affirmative	Negative
I / You live in Wales.	I / You don't live in Wales.
He / She / It lives in Wales.	He / She / It doesn't live in Wales.
We / You / They live in Wales.	We / You / They don't live in Wales.
Questions	
Do I / you live in Wales?	Where do I / you live?
Does he / she / it live in Wales?	Where does he / she / it live?
Do we / you / they live in Wales?	Where do we / you / they live?

Rules for spelling the third person singular (he / she / it) forms of verbs:

1 With most verbs, add -s to the base form.
   to walk — walks   to think — thinks
2 With verbs that end in consonant + -y, remove the -y and add -ies to the base form.
   to study — studies   to copy — copies
3 With verbs that end in -s, -z, -ch, -x and -o, add -es to the base form.
   to miss — misses   to watch — watches

Use

We use the present simple tense to:

1 Describe things that we do habitually or that occur regularly.
   She reads every evening.   It snows in December.
2 Talk about a permanent situation or a fact.
   I live in Glasgow.   I'm not British.
3 Express mental or emotional states, including likes and dislikes.
   Do you feel happy?   I like music.

Present continuous

Affirmative	Negative
I'm laughing.	I'm not laughing.
You're laughing.	You aren't laughing.
He's laughing.	He isn't laughing.
She's laughing.	She isn't laughing.
It's laughing.	It isn't laughing.
We're laughing.	We aren't laughing.
You're laughing.	You aren't laughing.
They're laughing.	They aren't laughing.

Questions	Short answers	
	Affirmative	Negative
Am I joking?	Yes, I am.	No, I'm not.
Are you joking?	Yes, you are.	No, you aren't.
Is he joking?	Yes, he is.	No, he isn't.
Is she joking?	Yes, she is.	No, she isn't.
Is it joking?	Yes, it is.	No, it isn't.
Are we joking?	Yes, we are.	No, we aren't.
Are you joking?	Yes, you are.	No, you aren't.
Are they joking?	Yes, they are.	No, they aren't.

Present simple and present continuous

Use

We use the present continuous to talk about actions in progress or future intentions.

He's interviewing a teacher. (at the moment)
I'm having dinner with a friend this evening. (later)

We use the present simple to talk about a routine or repeated action.

She has breakfast with her mum every morning.

Stative verbs

Some verbs are not usually used in the continuous form. (believe, belong, hate, imagine, know, like, love, prefer, remember, think, understand, and want.)

I love your bike. (NOT ~~I'm loving your new bike.~~)

Comparative and superlative adjectives

1   Complete the sentences using the comparative or superlative forms of the adjectives in brackets.

Maths is ___easier___ (easy) than science.

1   Who's _____ (good) tennis player in this class?
2   Roger Federer is _____ (famous) than me.
3   Gold isn't _____ (expensive) as platinum.
4   What's _____ (dangerous) sport?
5   This is _____ (rare) animal in the forest.
6   Your watch was _____ (cheap) than mine.
7   The station is _____ (near) as the bus stop.
8   Warsaw is _____ (large) city in Poland.
9   The weather got _____ (bad) during the day.
10 The plane is _____ (fast) way to travel.

Present simple

2   Complete the sentences using the present simple affirmative, negative or question forms of the verbs in brackets.

Where _does she live_ (she / live)?

1   I _____ (not like) the cinema.
2   Emilia _____ (wash up) every evening.
3   She _____ (not study) French.
4   _____ (you / cook)?
5   We _____ (not have) lunch at home.
6   My parents _____ (not work) on Saturdays.
7   When _____ (he / tidy) his room?
8   Susana _____ (watch) TV after school.
9   _____ (your mum / chat) to you?
10 What time _____ (your dad / go) to work?
11 He _____ (do) his homework every day.
12 You _____ (not finish) at 3.30.

Present continuous

3   Write affirmative or negative sentences, or questions, in the present continuous.

they / do / their homework /?
Are they doing their homework?

1   Isabela / look / at her phone
_____
2   you / listen / to the radio / ?
_____
3   we / laugh / at the film
_____
4   I / read / my book
_____
5   they / not walk / to school
_____
6   Jack / not sleep
_____
7   you / not do / the exercises
_____
8   we / watch / TV
_____
9   Tim and Nina / cycle / to school / ?
_____
10 she / carry / a bag
_____

Present simple and present continuous

4   Complete the sentences using the present simple or the present continuous form of the verbs in brackets.

Stop talking! I _'m doing_ (do) my homework.

1   They never _____ (get) the train home.
2   Look. Sofia _____ (help) her little brother.
3   We _____ (not have) dinner now.
4   I _____ (not wake up) early in the holidays.
5   Leon _____ (not call) his mum right now.
6   _____ (you / like) my mp3 player?
7   It _____ (not rain) now.
8   _____ (she / work) at the moment?
9   _____ (you / tidy) your room every day?
10 She _____ (not wear) jewellery today.

was, were, there was, there were

Affirmative	Negative
I was in the show.	I wasn't in the show.
You were in the show.	You weren't in the show.
He / She / It was in the show.	He / She / It wasn't in the show.
We / You / They were in the show.	We / You / They weren't in the show.
Questions	
Was I in the show?	
Were you in the show?	
Was he / she / it in the show?	
Were we / you / they in the show?	

	Affirmative	Negative
Singular	There was an advert.	There wasn't an advert.
Plural	There were some adverts.	There weren't any adverts.

Use

Was and *were* are the past simple forms of *be*. We use (*there*) *was* and (*there*) *were* to talk about past facts and opinions about the past.

They weren't in Gdańsk.   That was the best programme.

Past simple

Affirmative	Negative
I / You watched TV.	I / You didn't watch TV.
He / She / It watched TV.	He / She / It didn't watch TV.
We / You / They watched TV.	We / You / They didn't watch TV.
Questions	
Did I / you watch TV?	When did I / you watch TV?
Did he / she / it watch TV?	Where did he / she / it watch TV?
Did we / you / they watch TV?	Why did we / you / they watch TV?

Regular verbs

For most regular verbs, add *-ed*.
film   filmed
For regular verbs that end in *-e*, add *-d*.
smile   smiled
For regular verbs that end in vowel + consonant, double the consonant and add *-ed*.
travel   travelled

For regular verbs that end in consonant + *-y*, remove the *-y* and add *-ied*.
study   studied

Irregular verbs

See the list of irregular verbs on page 104.

Use

We use the past simple to describe a completed action in the past.
We watched the new Robert Pattinson film yesterday. Did you like it?
We use the past simple when we know when an action happened.
We watched TV on Monday. We didn't watch it on Tuesday.

Past continuous

Affirmative	Negative
I was walking.	I wasn't walking.
You were walking.	You weren't walking.
He / She / It was walking.	He / She / It wasn't walking.
We / You / They were walking.	We / You / They weren't walking.
Questions	
Was I walking?	Where was I walking?
Were you walking?	Where were you walking?
Was he / she / it walking?	Where was he / she / it walking?
Were we / you / they walking?	Where were we / you / they walking.

Use

We use the past continuous to describe the progress of an action in the past.
They were filming for three weeks.

Past simple and past continuous

Use

We use the past simple to talk about a completed action in the past.
I recorded *Friends* last Friday.
We use the past continuous to talk about an action that was in progress in the past.
I was watching a sports programme at 8 p.m.
We use the past continuous and the past simple together when one action interrupts another.
We usually use *while* with the past continuous and *when* with the past simple.
While I was watching TV, Joe arrived. = I was watching TV, when Joe arrived.

was, were, there was, there were

1 Complete the dialogue with the verbs in the box.

> there were   there weren't   was there
> there was   there wasn't   was   ~~was~~
> wasn't   were there

Tim What did you think about *1, 2, 3: You Pay Me!* on TV1? Did you like it?

Paul Yes, it ___was___ quite good, but the presenter [1]_____ as funny as Dale Summers.

Tim [2]_____ a lot of participants?

Paul No, [3]_____ many. In fact, [4]_____ only three.

Tim Who [5]_____ the winner?

Paul Mary Gallagher, from Wallingford.

Tim [6]_____ a good prize?

Paul Yes, [7]_____ a first prize of £25,000, but [8]_____ a second prize.

Past simple

2 Write sentences using the affirmative (✓), negative (✗) or question forms (?) of the past simple.

you / record / the cartoons **?**
___Did you record the cartoons?___

1 he / see / the first broadcast from the moon ✓
_____
_____

2 you / know / the presenter ✗
_____
_____

3 we / laugh / at the sitcom ✓
_____
_____

4 I / record / the right programme **?**
_____
_____

5 Lucy / go / to bed after the film **?**
_____

6 they / chat / about the news ✓
_____

7 I / take / the remote control ✗
_____

8 he / meet / the participants **?**
_____

Past continuous

3 Complete the sentences using the past continuous form of the verbs in brackets.

John ___was getting up___ (get up) at six o'clock.

1 You _____ (study) yesterday afternoon.

2 I _____ (not read) my book at ten o'clock last night.

3 I saw you at four o'clock. Where _____ (you / go)?

4 I _____ (not look) at you.

5 Who _____ (make) a noise last night?

6 We _____ (not watch) TV at five-thirty.

7 _____ (she / talk) to us?

8 Where _____ (they / go)?

9 My mum _____ (not drive) home.

10 How long _____ (they / wait) for the bus?

Past simple and past continuous

4 Write sentences using the past simple and past continuous tense.

while I / read / the phone / ring
___While I was reading, the phone rang.___

1 we / lose / the ball while we / play / football
_____
_____

2 when I / see / your sister / she / walk / to school
_____
_____

3 while Marek / do / his homework / his dad / come / home
_____
_____

4 they / run / when / I / see / them
_____

5 I / get / home / while you / cook
_____

6 she / dance / when / she / fall
_____

7 he / meet / a new friend / while / he / travel
_____

8 when I / see / you / you / talk / to / Mr Wood
_____
_____

much, many, a lot of, some, any

	Countable nouns	Uncountable nouns
Affirmative	There are a lot of apples.	There's a lot of juice.
Negative	There aren't many apples.	There isn't much juice.
Questions	How many apples are there?	How much juice is there?
Affirmative	There are some eggs.	There's some milk.
Negative	There aren't any eggs.	There isn't any milk.
Questions	Are there any eggs?	Is there any milk?

Use

We use *a lot of* to talk about countable and uncountable nouns in affirmative sentences.

There are a lot of plastic bags in the world.

There's a lot of rubbish, too.

We use *many* to talk about countable nouns in negative and interrogative sentences.

There aren't many cans of drink for the party.

Are there many cans of drink for the party?

We use *much* to talk about uncountable nouns in negative and interrogative sentences.

There isn't much milk for breakfast.

How much milk is there?

We use *some* to talk about countable and uncountable nouns in affirmative sentences.

There are some potatoes.

There's some sugar.

We use *any* to talk about countable and uncountable nouns in negative and interrogative sentences.

Are there any crisps? There aren't any crisps.

Is there any sugar? There isn't any sugar.

Relative pronouns

Relative pronoun	Used for ...
who	people
which	objects / ideas
where	places

Use

Relative pronouns tell us which person, object / idea or place is being talked about. They introduce new information. Without this information the sentence would be incomplete.

The man who lives next door recycles all his rubbish.

Did you see that film which was about the environment?

That's the local shop where we buy a lot of our food.

too, too much, too many, enough, not enough

Adjectives	Countable nouns	Uncountable nouns
The music is too quiet.	There are too many people.	There's too much rubbish.
Is it loud enough?	Are there enough packets of crisps?	Is there enough cola?
It is(n't) loud enough.	There are(n't) enough packets of crisps.	There is(n't) enough cola.

Use

too many / too much = more than necessary

enough = the necessary quantity

not enough = not sufficient

We use *too* before adjectives.

The music is too quiet.

We use *too many* before plural countable nouns.

There are too many big supermarkets in our town.

We use *too much* before uncountable nouns.

They drink too much coffee.

We use *(not) enough* after adjectives.

That box isn't big enough.

This box is big enough.

We use *(not) enough* before uncountable and plural countable nouns.

I eat enough fish.

I don't eat enough fish.

We can also use *(not) enough* with verbs. It goes after the verb.

He doesn't study enough.

much, many, a lot of, some, any

1 Complete the table with the words in the box.

> ~~sandwich~~ juice carton rubbish tea
> film washing powder packet jar
> music coffee food car book

Countable	Uncountable
sandwich	

2 Complete the sentences with *much, many* or *a lot of.*

I've got ____a lot of____ cool posters in my bedroom.

1 How _____ tubes of toothpaste do we need?

2 How _____ water do you drink every day?

3 There are _____ computers at your school.

4 How _____ newspapers do you buy every week?

5 They buy _____ magazines.

6 How _____ homework do your teachers give you?

7 How _____ people live in your home town?

3 Complete the dialogue with *some* or *any.*

Mark Have you got _____any_____ food for the party tonight?

Jack We've got ¹_____ crisps, but we haven't got ²_____ pizza.

Mark We also need ³_____ cans of fizzy drink.

Jack Yes. And we need ⁴_____ cups, too. There aren't ⁵_____ in the cupboard.

Mark Great. Have you got ⁶_____ money?

Jack Er ... no. I'll ask my mum for ⁷_____.

Relative pronouns

4 Write new sentences using one of the words in brackets.

You're the doctor. You helped us at the hospital. (where / who)
<u>You're the doctor who helped us at the hospital.</u>

1 This is the Tom Cruise film. It was on TV last night. (who / which)
_____
_____

2 That's the hotel. We stayed last year. (which / where)
_____
_____

3 She's the teacher. She gave us a lot of homework. (who / where)
_____
_____

4 This is the shop. I bought the bottle of shampoo. (where / which)
_____
_____

5 This is my little sister. She's learning to read and write. (which / who)
_____
_____

6 Here's the magazine. It was in my room. (who / which)
_____
_____

too, too much, too many, enough, not enough

5 Order the words to make sentences.

of / is / can / expensive / that / too / drink
<u>That can of drink is too expensive.</u>

1 got / food / drink / and / enough / we've
_____

2 throw / people / too / away / rubbish / much
_____

3 bags / waste / too / you / many / plastic
_____

4 enough / Jack / drink / doesn't / water
_____

5 that / is / coffee / enough / hot / ?
_____

6 shopping / big / isn't / bag / this / enough
_____

Present perfect: affirmative and negative

Affirmative	
Full forms	Short forms
I have searched.	I've searched.
You have searched.	You've searched.
He has played.	He's played.
She has played.	She's played.
It has played.	It's played.
We have blogged.	We've blogged.
You have blogged.	You've blogged.
They have blogged.	They've blogged.
Negative	
Full forms	Short forms
I have not searched.	I haven't searched.
You have not searched.	You haven't searched.
He has not played.	He hasn't played.
She has not played.	She hasn't played.
It has not played.	It hasn't played.
We have not blogged.	We haven't blogged.
You have not blogged.	You haven't blogged.
They have not blogged.	They haven't blogged.

In affirmative sentences, we usually use the short forms ('s / 've) in spoken English.
I've sent an email.
In negative sentences, we usually use short forms (*haven't / hasn't*) for both spoken and written English.
She hasn't been to London.
Do not confuse the short form of *has* ('s) with the short form of *is* (also 's).
He's had breakfast.
He's eating.

Use

We use the present perfect to talk about experiences that we have had or haven't had at some time in the past.
I've created a website.
She's uploaded some photos.
You haven't visited that chat room.
We never use the present perfect to talk about an event that happened at a specific time in the past. We use it when the time of the event is not important or is not known.
She's been to Australia.

Present perfect: regular and irregular verbs

For regular verbs, the past participle is the same as the past simple form. See the rules for the formation of regular -ed endings on page 74. There are no rules for the formation of irregular verbs. You have to learn the form whenever you learn a new verb. Here are some typical irregular verb patterns.

Infinitive	Past simple	Past participle
Past simple and past participle with the same forms		
catch	caught	caught
have	had	had
All forms the same		
put	put	put
cut	cut	cut
Different vowels: $i \rightarrow a \rightarrow u$		
begin	began	begun
Participle ends -n or -en		
break	broke	broken
Exceptions		
do	did	done
go	went	gone

See the list of irregular verbs on page 104.

Present perfect: questions

Questions	
Have I chatted with you?	Where have I been?
Have you chatted with him?	Where have you been?
Has he been with us?	Where has he been?
Has she been with us?	Where has she been?
Has it been with us?	Where has it been?
Have we chatted?	Why have we stopped?
Have you chatted?	Why have you stopped?
Have they chatted?	Why have they stopped?

Use

We use the present perfect to ask about past experiences. We sometimes use *ever* in questions to mean 'at any time in your life until this moment'.
Have you ever played an online game?
Has she ever downloaded a film?

Present perfect: affirmative and negative

1 Write sentences using the present perfect.

I / not email / you
I haven't emailed you.

1 she / create / a great webpage
_____
_____

2 we / not cycle / to school
_____
_____

3 he / not study / French
_____

4 it / not save / the files
_____

5 I / use / a smartphone
_____

6 they / not log on / to your webpage
_____
_____

7 you / email / the club
_____

8 he / not share / the files
_____
_____

Present perfect: regular and irregular verbs

2 Complete the sentences using the present perfect form of the verbs in brackets.

He ___hasn't felt___ (not feel) well for a long time.

1 You _____ (eat) all my chocolates!
2 They _____ (sell) a lot of DVDs.
3 I _____ (not travel) to the USA.
4 She _____ (meet) Kylie Minogue.
5 We _____ (not write) an essay.
6 It _____ (copy) two hundred files.
7 You _____ (not make) any money.
8 James _____ (fly) in a plane.
9 We _____ (run) five kilometres.
10 Maria _____ (drink) mango juice.
11 My cousins _____ (not chat) on the internet.
12 I _____ (spend) all my money.

Present perfect: questions

3 Write questions using the present perfect.

where / they / stay
Where have they stayed?

1 who / take / my box
_____

2 which / films / you / see
_____

3 what / you / buy
_____

4 where / she / live
_____

5 which / books / you / read
_____

6 why / Tim / sell / his laptop
_____

7 how / they / travel
_____

8 what / you / send
_____

4 Write questions using the present perfect and *have you ever*. Then write true answers.

message anyone?
Have you ever messaged anyone?
Yes, I've messaged my best friend a lot. /
No, I've never messaged anyone.

1 blog
_____
_____

2 chat online
_____
_____

3 buy a laptop
_____
_____

4 download music
_____
_____

5 create a personal webpage
_____
_____

6 upload files
_____
_____

Adverbs of degree

Use

We use adverbs of degree such as: *a bit, incredibly, not very, quite, really* and *very*, before adjectives and adverbs to add the idea of 'how much'.

That CD is a bit expensive.

I'm incredibly hungry.

He isn't very tolerant.

Note that we can only use these adverbs with gradable adjectives. For example, *interesting* is gradable – books can be more or less interesting. But we can't use these adverbs with non-gradable adjectives such as *impossible* or *dead*.

Present perfect + *still, yet, just* and *already*

Use

We use *just, still, yet* and *already* with the present perfect.

Just is used to reinforce the idea that an action has only been completed very recently. It is used in affirmative sentences, and comes between the auxiliary *has / have* and the past participle.

She's just won a talent show.

We've just met that film star.

We use *still* to reinforce the idea that something hasn't changed. It is used in negative sentences and it comes before *has / have*.

It's very late, but you still haven't done your homework.

I still haven't watched that new DVD.

We use *yet* in negative sentences and questions to talk about something that hasn't happened but that we expect to happen. It comes at the end of the phrase.

They haven't bought the concert tickets yet. (But we think they will soon.)

Has he finished his new album yet? (We think he will finish it soon.)

We use *already* with the present perfect to show that something has happened before now. It comes between the auxiliary *has / have* and the past participle.

We've already seen that singer in concert.

She's already read that magazine.

Present perfect + *for* and *since*

Use

For can be used with the present perfect or the past simple.

With the present perfect, *for* describes the duration of an action or event which started in the past and continues into the present. It is followed by a period of time: *for three months, for five days*, etc. It is placed before the time expression:

She's worked here for five years. (And she still works here.)

Ben has been in the band for two years. (And he's still in it.)

With the past simple *for* describes an action which started and finished in the past.

She worked here for five years. (But she doesn't work here now.)

Adrian was in the band for six months. (But he isn't in it now.)

Since is used with the present perfect, and it tells you when an action started. It is placed before the time expression.

He's lived in this town since 2009.

We've known Laura since May.

Present perfect and past simple

Use

The past simple is used to talk about an action or a period of time in the past which is completed.

We watched that new pop video this afternoon. (It is now evening.)

He played tennis at two o'clock. (He isn't playing tennis now.)

The present perfect is used to describe events which started in the past and continue in the present.

We've had this car for three years. (And we've still got it.)

You've studied at this school since 2010. (And you're still studying here.)

Different time expressions are used with each form.

The past simple uses time expressions which pinpoint specific moments in the past: *yesterday, last night, last week, last year, at six o'clock*, etc.

The present perfect uses expressions which describe the point at which an action started, or a period of time.

Adverbs of degree

1 Rewrite the first sentence using one of the adverbs in brackets.

We're tired. But we can play two more games of tennis. (very / a bit)

We're a bit tired.

1 She goes to bed late. Usually at two o'clock in the morning. (really / not very)

_____

2 This exam is difficult. I can't do any of the questions. (a bit / incredibly)

_____

3 The tickets for the concert are expensive. They're £200. (quite / very)

_____

4 He's tall. But a lot of people are taller than him. (quite / incredibly)

_____

5 This film is interesting. I don't want to watch it. (not very / really)

_____

6 We're hungry. So can we have a snack, please? (a bit / not very)

_____

Present perfect + *still*, *yet*, *just* and *already*

2 Order the words to make sentences and questions.

comic / have / you / finished / yet / this / ?

Have you finished this comic yet?

1 to / still / bed / hasn't / Emma / gone

_____

_____

2 already / bought / I've / CD / that

_____

3 have / to / been / they / yet / Paris / ?

_____

4 tidied / the / still / they / haven't / classroom

_____

_____

5 show / already / started / the / has

_____

_____

6 hasn't / my / yet / woken up / brother

_____

_____

Present perfect + *for* and *since*

3 Complete the phrases with *for* or *since*.

___*for*___ three months

1 _____ last August

2 _____ a few weeks

3 _____ yesterday

4 _____ 1998

5 _____ about six years

6 _____ I was ten

7 _____ a long time

4 Complete the sentences using the present perfect form of the verbs in the box and *for* or *since*.

> not see   ~~live~~   not do   play   not appear
> learn   work

She *'s lived* in Rome ___*for*___ five years.

1 The singers _____ on TV _____ 2009.

2 You _____ in that restaurant _____ five months.

3 He _____ for the same team _____ he was twelve.

4 I _____ my cousins _____ October.

5 We _____ any homework _____ two weeks.

6 He _____ English _____ three years.

Present perfect and past simple

5 Complete the sentences using the present perfect or past simple form of the verbs in brackets.

She __*hasn't had*__ (not have) a holiday for six months.

1 I _____ (stay) in that hotel when I was a child.

2 He's very intelligent. He _____ (pass) all his exams last year.

3 We _____ (be) at this school since we were five years old.

4 _____ (you / try) Japanese food?

5 I _____ (see) that Brad Pitt film at Christmas.

6 _____ (they / visit) Portugal last July?

should and *must*

Should and *must* have got the same form for all subject pronouns.
I should, you shouldn't, he must, she mustn't, etc.
We use *should* and *must* with the base form of the main verb.
You should get good qualifications. (NOT ~~You should to get good qualifications.~~)
You mustn't cheat in the exam. (NOT ~~You mustn't to cheat in the exam.~~)

Use

We use *should* to ask for or give advice or a recommendation.
You should study harder.
You shouldn't stay up so late.
We use *must* to talk about something that is important, a rule or a law.
You must wear a motorbike helmet.
You mustn't write in pen.

have to and *don't have to*

Affirmative	Negative
I / You have to work.	I / You don't have to work.
He / She / It has to work.	He / She / It doesn't have to work.
We / You / They have to work.	We / You / They don't have to work.

We use *have to* with the base form of the main verb.

Use

We use *have to* to talk about something that is necessary to do, for example, when it is a rule or because of circumstances.
At my school, we have to wear a uniform.
She has to catch a bus to school. (It's too far to walk.)
We use *don't have to* to talk about something that is not necessary to do.
We don't have to walk far to school because we live close to school.

should, *must* and *have to*

Recommendation
You should revise for the exam.
You shouldn't copy your homework.

Obligation
You must arrive at 9 a.m.
You mustn't be late.
We have to wear a uniform.

No obligation
You don't have to wear a tie.

Use

Must and *have to* have got almost the same meaning.
I must do my homework tonight. = I have to do my homework tonight.
We often use *must* to talk about something that the speaker decides is necessary.
You must do your homework now.
We often use *have to* when other circumstances make something necessary.
I have to go to the library because I need some books.
We use *don't have to* to talk about something that is not necessary to do.
We don't have to clean the house. (because it is already clean).
Remember: *don't have to* doesn't mean the same as *mustn't*.
You mustn't write in pen. = It's a rule.
You don't have to write in pen. = It's not necessary.

should and must

1 Complete the sentences with *must, mustn't, should* or *shouldn't*.

You ___must___ buy a ticket before you go into the cinema.

1 You _____ watch the new Will Smith film if you can get tickets. It's great.
2 They _____ wear sports clothes in the gym or they won't be allowed to play.
3 You _____ lose your keys. We don't have another set.
4 She _____ borrow so much money. She _____ save her pocket money.
5 He _____ relax. The exams have finished.
6 You _____ bully people.
7 We _____ copy our homework from the internet.
8 They _____ worry. I'm sure everything will be fine.

have to and don't have to

2 Complete the sentences using the affirmative, negative, or question form of *have to* and the verbs in brackets.

Roman ___doesn't have to sign___ (not sign) a new contract.

1 _____ (you / finish) your essay today?
2 They _____ (not wear) a uniform.
3 You _____ (not leave) school when you're sixteen.
4 Lily is annoyed. She _____ (stay) with her little brother this weekend.
5 The pass mark is 70%. You _____ (get) 70% to pass the exam.
6 The essays _____ (not be) long.
7 _____ (the dog / sleep) here?
8 I _____ (not get up) early tomorrow.
9 We _____ (bring) our two favourite songs to class tomorrow.
10 She _____ (not do) extra English classes.

should, must and have to

3 Order the words to make sentences and questions.

you / have / to / to / school / seven / at / o'clock / do / go / ?

Do you have to go to school at seven o'clock?

1 bed / to / earlier / go / she / should

_____

2 mustn't / corridors / the / in / school / run / you

_____

3 go / doesn't / have / work / she / to / to / yet

_____

4 I / to / dog / must / the / remember / walk

_____

5 revise / for / exam / have / he / to / the / does / ?

_____

6 shouldn't / wear / you / boots / at / school

_____

7 don't / we / have / go / to / to / Saturday / on / school

_____
_____

8 should / bring / some / the / picnic / food / they / to / ?

_____
_____

4 Complete the sentences using the correct form of *should, must* or *have to*.

We ___don't have to___ walk to school. We go by car.

1 We _____ wear jeans at school. We've got a uniform.
2 _____ we _____ speak English in the classroom?
3 You _____ copy your friend's homework. It isn't fair.
4 You _____ take things that aren't yours.
5 He looks ill. He _____ see a doctor.
6 We _____ get the bus at three-thirty. It's the last bus.
7 You _____ pay me now. You can pay me tomorrow.
8 Tomas _____ go to school. He's nineteen.
9 The team _____ practise more. There's an important match next week.
10 If you're tired, you _____ go to bed.

will and might

Affirmative	Negative	Interrogative
I / You / He / She / It / We / You / They will help.	I / You / He / She / It / We / You / They won't help.	Will I / you / he / she / it / we / you / they help?

Affirmative	Negative
I / You / He / She / It / We / You / They might help.	I / You / He / She / It / We / You / They might not help.

Will and *might* are used with the base form of the verb.

We'll join the protest next week.

I might bring Anna.

The negative is formed by putting *not* after *will* or *might*.

Will not is usually contracted to *won't*. *Might not* is not usually contracted.

I won't be at the meeting tomorrow.

Jake might not come because he's ill.

Use

We use *will* and *won't* to predict or give our opinion about the future. We normally use *will* and *won't* to talk about something definite or when we are very sure about our opinion.

I'll meet you outside school.

We use *might* and *might not* for something that is possible or when we are not sure.

It might be hot at the weekend.

First conditional

Affirmative	Negative
If you go to the meeting, you'll see Joshua.	If I don't go to the meeting, I won't see Adele.
If he walks fast, he'll be on time.	If she doesn't walk fast, she won't meet David.
If we study hard, we'll go to university.	If they don't study hard, they won't get a good job.

We form the first conditional with *if* + subject + present simple, + subject + *will / won't* + infinitive. We normally use the contracted forms.

The *if* clause can also come in the second half of the sentence.

If you come on the march, you'll meet Fatima.

You'll meet Fatima if you come on the march.

Use

We use the first conditional to talk about possible situations and the probable results of actions.

If it rains, we won't play tennis.

We'll collect a lot of money if we get a lot of sponsors.

be going to and will

Affirmative	Negative
I'm going to protest.	I'm not going to protest.
You're going to protest.	You aren't going to protest.
He's / She's / It's going to protest.	He / She / It isn't going to protest.
We're / You're / They're going to protest.	We / You / They aren't going to protest.

We form the affirmative with the subject + *be* + *going to* + the infinitive.

We form the negative with the subject + *be* + *not going to* + the infinitive.

Interrogative
Am I going to study?
Are you going to study?
Is he / she / it going to study?
Are we / you / they going to study?

Use

We use *will* and *be going to* to talk about the future.

We use *will* to predict or give our opinion about the future.

The meeting will be interesting.

We use *be going to* to talk about plans and intentions for the future.

She's going to collect money for animals in danger.

I'm going to campaign for a new school building.

Present continuous for future arrangements

The present continuous is used to talk about arrangements with a fixed date or time in the future.

I'm playing tennis on Friday morning.

We aren't seeing Laura this evening.

What are you doing tomorrow?

Are you staying at home this afternoon?

UNIT 6 ● LANGUAGE FOCUS PRACTICE

will and *might*

1 Rewrite the sentences using *will*, *won't*, *might* and *might not*.

Karl (collect) a lot of money today. (maybe not)
<u>Karl might not collect a lot of money today.</u>

1 Lucy (support) your campaign. (definitely)

_____

2 They (boycott) that supermarket. (maybe)

_____

3 I (sign) your petition. (definitely not)

_____

4 He (volunteer) to help us. (maybe not)

_____

5 Asif (come) to the meeting. (definitely not)

_____

6 We (protest) against the new road. (maybe)

_____

First conditional

2 Choose the correct words.

(They'll)/ They listen to us if **we'll** /(we)protest.

1 If it **will rain / rains** on Sunday, we **won't / don't** go on the march.

2 You **won't / don't** save the rainforest if **you'll / you** sit and do nothing.

3 If **she'll work / she works** hard, **she'll do / she does** well at school.

4 **Will / Do** you support my campaign if **I'll / I** tell you about it?

5 If we **won't / don't** look after the environment, **we'll / we** have problems in the future.

6 **I'll / I** give you a poster, if **you'll / you** sign up to our newsletter.

be going to and *will*

3 Complete the sentences. Use the affirmative of *will* or *be going to* and the verbs in brackets.

When we get home, we <u>'re going to have</u> (have) dinner.

1 I know they _____ (feel) very happy if they win the match.

2 They've already decided on their next holiday. They _____ (do) a tour of Canada.

3 Why is Lydia worried?
She _____ (take) her driving test this afternoon.

4 If you revise for the exam, I'm sure you _____ (get) a good result.

5 She thinks that the *Sugababes* concert _____ (be) really exciting.

6 What are your plans for this evening?
I _____ (meet) Clara and then we _____ (go) to a party.

Present continuous for future arrangements

4 Write questions and answers using the present continuous.

what / you / do / this evening

I / watch / TV

<u>What are you doing this evening?</u>

<u>I'm watching TV.</u>

1 your dad / work / tomorrow
no / he / stay / at home

_____

_____

2 what / they / cook / on Sunday
they / make / a pizza

_____

_____

3 who / you / see / tonight
I / meet / Paula and Anna

_____

_____

4 where / we / go / at the weekend
we / visit / Aunt Sarah

_____

_____

5 Gabriella / come / with us / later
no / she / look after / her sister

_____

_____

6 you / catch / the bus / today
no / I / walk / to school

_____

_____

Verbs + -ing / to

Verb			+ -ing
I / You We / You / They	like / don't like love prefer		walking.
He / She	likes / doesn't like loves prefers		reading. living here.
Do Does Do	I / you he / she we / you / they	like love prefer	walking? reading? living here?

Verb			+ to
I / You He / She We / You They	would / 'd wouldn't	like love prefer	to walk. to read. to live here.
Would	I / you he / she we / you / they	like love prefer	to walk there? to read this? to live here?

Use

We use *like / love / prefer* + *-ing* to talk or ask about likes, dislikes and preferences.

I love riding my bike.   We prefer running.

We don't usually use *love* or *prefer* in negative sentences.

She doesn't like watching films.

We use *would* + verb + *to* + main verb to express or ask about desires or make suggestions.

We'd like to go to the cinema.

Would you like to go to the cinema?

could, can, will be able to

Affirmative		
Past	Present	Future
I could speak Italian.	She can speak Italian.	They will be able to speak Italian.

Negative		
Past	Present	Future
We couldn't speak Italian.	You can't speak Italian.	He won't be able to speak Italian.

Questions		
Past	Present	Future
Could you speak Italian?	Can he speak Italian?	Will they be able to speak Italian?

We use *could*, *can* and *will be able to* with the base form of the verb.

Could, *can* and *will be able to* have the same form for all subject pronouns.

Use

We use *could*, *can* and *will be able to* to express ability or possibility.

Past: **I couldn't speak English when I was very young.**

Present: **I can speak English because I am from the UK.**

Future: **I won't be able to go cycling because I'm ill.**

Second conditional

Affirmative
If I / you got up earlier, I / you wouldn't be late.
If he / she acted well, he / she would get a good review.
If we / you / they studied more, we / you / they would get better marks.

Negative
If I / you didn't go to bed late, I / you wouldn't be so tired.
If he / she / it didn't act badly, he / she / it wouldn't get a bad review.
If we / you / they didn't watch TV all night, we / you / they would go out.

Questions
If you got up earlier, would you walk to school?
If he / she / it acted well, would he / she / it get a good review?
If we / you / they studied more, would we / you / they get better marks?

We form the second conditional with *if* + subject + past simple + comma (,) + *would / wouldn't* + base form. We normally use the contracted forms.

The *if* clause can come in the second half of the sentence. The meaning is the same, but we do not need a comma.

I'd be on time if I got up earlier. = If I got up earlier, I'd be on time.

If he posted a message, I'd reply. = I'd reply if he posted a message.

We form information questions with the question word at the beginning of the *would* clause.

What files would you share if you were online? = If you were online, what files would you share?

Use

We use the second conditional to talk about hypothetical, unreal or imaginary situations.

If I had £200, I'd buy a mobile phone. (I haven't got £200, so I won't buy a mobile phone.)

Verbs + -ing / to

1 Complete the dialogues using the *to* or *-ing* forms of the verbs in brackets.

Fiona Do you like ___dancing___ (dance)?

Gary Not really. I prefer ¹_____ (listen) to music.

Fiona Would you like ²_____ (listen) to some music now?

Gary Sure, I'd love to.

Sue I'd like ³_____ (go) out tonight.

Mary I'd prefer ⁴_____ (stay) at home. I don't like ⁵_____ (go) out on school nights.

Sue But you like ⁶_____ (watch) *Oxford United* matches!

Mary Is there a match tonight?

Sue Yes, there is. Do you want ⁷_____ (come)?

Mary Yes, I've changed my mind! I'd love ⁸_____ (watch) the match with you!

could, can, will be able to

2 Complete the sentences using the correct affirmative or negative forms of *could*, *can* or *will be able to*.

My mum grew up in France. She ___could___ speak French when she was very young.

1 In Britain you _____ drive a car until you're seventeen.

2 It's June. We _____ go to the beach soon.

3 I _____ cycle when I was five, but now I cycle every day.

4 Where are you? I _____ see you.

5 _____ (you) drive when you're older?

6 I _____ create personal webpages. I've created one for my dad.

7 _____ you speak English ten years ago?

8 I _____ run faster than my sister when we were younger, but she's faster than me now.

9 I _____ call you last night because I've lost your phone number.

10 You _____ make some new friends when you start at your new school.

Second conditional

3 Complete the sentences with the words in the box.

> took ~~do~~ had if save went
> would wouldn't

What would you ___do___ if I told you a secret?

1 She wouldn't be nervous if she _____ the exam. She always does well.

2 If we _____ to Paris, what museums would we visit?

3 _____ Sam complained, we'd say sorry.

4 _____ they tidy their rooms if you paid them?

5 You'd _____ paper if you printed on both sides.

6 If you _____ £200, what would you buy?

7 If you didn't have a bike, you _____ cycle to school.

4 Write sentences and questions using the second conditional.

your mum / lend / you money / if / you / ask / her / ?

Would your mum lend you money if you asked her?

1 if / we / pass / all the exams / our teacher / be / really happy

_____

2 I / give / you the money / if / I / have / it

_____

3 what / they / do / if / we / offer / them a choice / ?

_____

4 if / John / find / some money / he / give / it / to the teacher

_____

5 if / you / get / the job / you / be / happy / ?

_____

6 I / come / to your party / if / I / not have / an exam

_____

Present and past passive: affirmative and negative

Present passive

Affirmative	Negative
I'm sent a lot of emails.	I'm not sent a lot of emails.
You're sent a lot of emails.	You aren't sent a lot of emails.
He's / She's / It's sent a lot of emails.	He / She / It isn't sent a lot of emails.
We're / You're / They're sent a lot of emails.	We / You / They aren't sent a lot of emails.

We form the present passive affirmative with the subject + present simple of *be* + past participle. We form the present passive negative with the subject + present simple of *be* + *not* + past participle.

Past passive

Affirmative	Negative
I was woken up by the music.	I wasn't woken up by the music.
You were woken up by the music.	You weren't woken up by the music.
He / She / It was woken up by the music.	He / She / It wasn't woken up by the music.
We / You / They were woken up by the music.	We / You / They weren't woken up by the music.

We form the past passive affirmative with the subject + past simple of *be* + past participle. We form the past passive negative with the subject + past simple of *be* + *not* + past participle.

Use

Passive sentences emphasize the action. The action is more important than the person who does the action. Often the person is unknown so it is not included.

The TV programme about Picasso was made in France.
If we change an active sentence to a passive sentence, the object of the active sentence becomes the subject of a passive sentence.

People paint these pictures in Japan. = These pictures are painted in Japan.

Emma invited Susie to the new art gallery. = Susie was invited to the new art gallery.

In passive sentences, we don't often say who carried out the action. When we do, we use *by*.
Susie was invited to the new art gallery by Emma.

Present passive questions

Questions	Short answers	
	Affirmative	Negative
Am I sent a lot of emails?	Yes, I am.	No, I'm not.
Are you sent a lot of emails?	Yes, you are.	No, you aren't.
Is he / she / it sent a lot of emails?	Yes, he / she / it is.	No, he / she / it isn't.
Are we / you / they sent a lot of emails?	Yes, we / you / they are.	No, we / you / they aren't.

We form present passive questions with the present simple of *be* + subject + past participle.
Are you invited to the party at the museum?
Is she paid a lot of money for her sculptures?

Past passive questions

Questions	Short answers	
	Affirmative	Negative
Was I woken up by the music?	Yes, I was.	No, I wasn't.
Were you woken up by the music?	Yes, you were.	No, you weren't.
Was he / she / it woken up by the music?	Yes, he / she / it was.	No, he / she / it wasn't.
Were we / you / they woken up by the music?	Yes, we / you / they were.	No, we / you / they weren't.

We form past passive questions with the past simple of *be* + subject + past participle.
Were we given some information at the art gallery?
Was he told about the new Van Gogh exhibition?

Present passive: affirmative and negative

1 Complete the sentences using the present passive form of the verbs in brackets.

Beautiful cakes __are made__ (make) in France.

1 Oranges _____ (not grow) in cold countries.
2 Ice hockey _____ (watch) by millions of TV viewers in Canada.
3 Chocolates _____ (make) in Belgium.
4 Our car _____ (not clean) every week.
5 Laptops _____ (not allow) in our classroom.
6 French _____ (not speak) much in the USA.
7 Our dog _____ (give) food twice a day.

2 Complete the sentences using the present passive form of the verbs in the box.

> eat   visit   invite   make   use
> ~~find~~   play

Gold __is found__ in South Africa.

1 Mobile phones _____ by a lot of people nowadays.
2 Football _____ in different countries around the world.
3 Millions of pizzas _____ every week in the USA.
4 Paper _____ from trees.
5 A lot of people _____ to parties at Christmas.
6 London _____ by millions of tourists every year.

Past passive

3 Complete the second sentence so that it has the same meaning as the first sentence. Use the past passive.

Leonardo da Vinci created this sculpture.
This sculpture was created by Leonardo da Vinci.

1 Somebody stole the Monet painting last month.
The Monet painting _____
_____.

2 Gaudí designed this building.
This building _____
_____.

3 They didn't invite us to the art gallery.
We _____
_____.

4 Nobody cleaned our hotel room this morning.
Our hotel room _____
_____.

5 Somebody sent me a book about modern art.
I _____
_____.

6 They didn't tell her the terrible news.
She _____
_____.

7 Somebody gave us a tour of the museum.
We _____.

Present and past passive: affirmative, negative and questions

4 Write sentences and questions using the present or past passive.

these CDs / advertise on the internet / ?
Are these CDs advertised on the internet?

1 Mandarin / teach / at your school / now / ?
_____
_____

2 presents / give / at Christmas
_____
_____

3 this picture / buy / by a collector / yesterday
_____
_____

4 those portraits / paint / by Renoir / ?
_____
_____

5 football shirts / not sell / in this shop
_____
_____

6 the missing pictures / not found / for a long time
_____
_____

7 where / your bag / steal / last week / ?
_____
_____

PRONUNCIATION BANK

Unit 1: Past tense -*ed* endings

1 🔘 1.02 **Listen and repeat.**

1 /d/ played
2 /t/ laughed
3 /ɪd/ chatted

2 🔘 1.03 **Complete the table with the verbs in the box. Listen and check your answers. Then listen again and repeat.**

> ~~argued~~ ~~connected~~ ~~finished~~ watched
> complained cried introduced offered
> recorded pushed respected shouted
> showed stayed stopped visited
> talked wanted

/d/	/t/	/ɪd/
argued	finished	connected

3 🔘 1.04 **Listen and tick ✓ the word you hear.**

1 ☐ cry   ☐ cried
2 ☐ finish   ☐ finished
3 ☐ shout   ☐ shouted
4 ☐ respect   ☐ respected
5 ☐ talk   ☐ talked
6 ☐ laugh   ☐ laughed
7 ☐ push   ☐ pushed
8 ☐ introduce ☐ introduced

4 🔘 1.05 **Read and circle the odd word out. Then listen and repeat.**

1 started   completed liked   attracted
2 organized lived   received escaped
3 tried   passed   looked   announced
4 cleaned   listened   carried   laughed
5 played   decided   chatted   waited
6 practised worked   shopped   arrived

Unit 2: Word stress in compound nouns

1 🔘 1.06 **Listen and repeat.**

1 shopping bag
2 science exam
3 strawberry ice cream
4 phone call

2 🔘 1.07 **Listen and <u>underline</u> the stress in the words.**

1 football shirt
2 washing powder
3 computer game
4 tourist office
5 Christmas present
6 magazine cover
7 maths book
8 basketball match
9 birthday card
10 documentary series

3 **Practise saying these words.**

1 washing powder
2 coffee cup
3 kitchen paper
4 orange juice

4 **Practise saying these sentences.**

1 Would you like a chicken sandwich?
2 I like strawberry ice cream.
3 Is there any kitchen paper?
4 There's a big shopping centre.

Unit 3: Vowels

1 🔘 1.08 **Listen and repeat.**

/æ/	/ʌ/
drank	drunk
began	begun
ran	run
rang	rung
sang	sung
swam	swum

2 🔘 1.09 **Listen and tick ✓ the word you hear.**

1 ☐ rung   ☐ rang
2 ☐ ran   ☐ run
3 ☐ swum   ☐ swam
4 ☐ drank ☐ drunk
5 ☐ sang   ☐ sung
6 ☐ begun ☐ began

3 🔘 1.10 **Listen and check your answers.**

PRONUNCIATION BANK

Unit 4: Diphthongs /əʊ/ /eə/ /aɪ/ /aʊ/

1 🔊 1.11 Listen and repeat the diphthongs and the words.

1 /əʊ/ phone
2 /eə/ there
3 /aɪ/ nice
4 /aʊ/ brown

2 🔊 1.12 Listen and repeat the words in the box. Then complete the table.

photo̶ square now like OK town
go guy wear about chair mind

/əʊ/	/eə/	/aɪ/	/aʊ/
photo	_____	_____	_____
_____	_____	_____	_____
_____	_____	_____	_____

3 🔊 1.13 Listen and check your answers.

4 Write the correct diphthong next to the sentences below. Practise saying them.

1 She's got **fair hair**. _____
2 He's **quite shy**. _____
3 **Our house** is in town. _____
4 We **don't know**. _____

Unit 5: Weak forms

1 🔊 1.14 Listen and repeat. Notice the weak forms /tə/ and /ðə/.

/tə//ðə/
1 You shouldn't go to the sports centre today.
/ðə/ /tə/ /ðə/
2 The new students have to wear the green uniform.
/tə//ðə/
3 I must go to the library.
/tə/ /ðə/
4 She has to do the homework later.

2 🔊 1.15 Listen and circle the weak forms /tə/ and /ðə/ in each sentence.

1 We have to visit Grandma.
2 Let's go past the post office.
3 The uniforms weren't very nice.
4 You mustn't run in the corridor.
5 I went to primary school in South Street.
6 Is this the book she wanted?

3 🔊 1.16 Circle the weak forms /tə/ and /ðə/. Listen and check.

Some parents want to send their children to single-sex schools, but the majority of British teenagers go to mixed schools. Students have to stay at school until the school-leaving age, which is sixteen.

Unit 6: Linking

1 🔊 1.17 Listen and repeat. Pay attention to the linking sounds.

1 Let's organize a protest.
2 They must ban all violent games.
3 That's a good idea.
4 Shall we have a meeting for an hour?
5 How about starting the boycott on Saturday?

2 🔊 1.18 Listen and draw the linking sounds in the sentences.

We've got a new petition.

1 Come on this march with us!
2 Let's send an email now.
3 There's a lot of litter here.
4 Shall we meet at ten o'clock?
5 You can ask your brother or sister.

3 🔊 1.18 Listen again to the sentences in exercise 2 and repeat them. Use the linking sounds.

4 Mark the linking sounds in these short phrases. Then practise saying them.

1 Find out some information.
2 Support our campaign.
3 Join in with us.
4 Sign up in April.

PRONUNCIATION BANK

Unit 7: Silent letters

1 🔘 1.19 We do not pronounce every consonant in some words. Listen and repeat.

1	column	5	character
2	school	6	sign
3	listen	7	would
4	might	8	mustn't

2 🔘 1.20 Cross out the consonants that we do not pronounce. Then listen and check.

1	thumb	6	ghost
2	receipt	7	scent
3	design	8	autumn
4	island	9	talk
5	know	10	wrist

3 🔘 1.21 Circle two words in each sentence with consonants that we do not pronounce. Listen and check.

1 There were some frightening scenes in the novel.
2 Did you walk or climb up the mountain?
3 That wasn't the right answer, was it?
4 I bought him two great birthday presents.
5 We have to write a talk and present it next week.
6 You shouldn't play with knives.

Unit 8: Word stress

1 🔘 1.22 Listen and match the words with the stress patterns. Then listen again and repeat.

1	painting	a	•●•
2	gallery	b	●•
3	museum	c	•●
4	exhibition	d	•●••
5	collect	e	●••
6	impressionist	f	••●•

2 Complete the table with the words in the box.

portrait collector education support accept masterpiece landscape photography president definition important intelligent

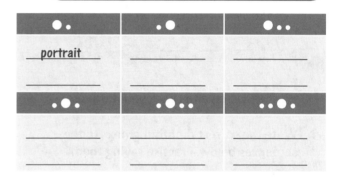

●•	•●	●••
portrait		

•●•	•●••	••●•

3 🔘 1.23 Listen and check your answers. Then listen and repeat.

4 Draw the stress patterns for these adjectives. Use a dictionary to help you.

1 colourful
2 shocking
3 provocative
4 imaginative
5 amusing

Phonetic symbols

Vowels

/i/	happy
/ɪ/	it
/iː/	he
/æ/	flag
/ɑː/	art
/e/	egg
/ɜː/	her
/ɒ/	not
/ɔː/	four
/ʊ/	look
/uː/	you
/ə/	sugar
/ʌ/	mum
/eɪ/	day
/aɪ/	why
/ɔɪ/	noisy
/aʊ/	how
/əʊ/	go
/ɪə/	here
/eə/	wear
/ʊə/	tourist

Consonants

/p/	pen
/b/	big
/t/	two
/d/	dog
/k/	can
/g/	good
/tʃ/	beach
/dʒ/	job
/f/	food
/v/	very
/θ/	think
/ð/	then
/s/	speak
/z/	zoo
/ʃ/	she
/ʒ/	television
/h/	house
/m/	meat
/n/	now
/ŋ/	sing
/l/	late
/r/	radio
/j/	yes
/w/	we

Starter unit

boring (adj)   /ˈbɔːrɪŋ/
cheap (adj)   /tʃiːp/
clean (adj)   /kliːn/
common (adj)   /ˈkɒmən/
cook (v)   /kʊk/
dangerous (adj)   /ˈdeɪndʒərəs/
difficult (adj)   /ˈdɪfɪkəlt/
dirty (adj)   /ˈdɜːti/
do your homework (v)   /ˌduː jɔː ˈhəʊmwɜːk/
easy (adj)   /ˈiːzi/
exciting (adj)   /ɪkˈsaɪtɪŋ/
expensive (adj)   /ɪkˈspensɪv/
far (adj)   /fɑː(r)/
finish (v)   /ˈfɪnɪʃ/
get home (v)   /ˌget ˈhəʊm/
get the bus (v)   /ˌget ðə ˈbʌs/
get up (v)   /ˌget ˈʌp/
go shopping (v)   /ˌgəʊ ˈʃɒpɪŋ/
go to bed (v)   /ˌgəʊ tə ˈbed/
go to sleep (v)   /ˌgəʊ tə ˈsliːp/
go to work (v)   /ˌgəʊ tə ˈwɜːk/
have breakfast (v)   /ˌhæv ˈbrekfəst/
healthy (adj)   /ˈhelθi/
heavy (adj)   /ˈhevi/
light (adj)   /laɪt/
near (adj)   /nɪə(r)/
noisy (adj)   /ˈnɔɪzi/
play (v)   /pleɪ/
powerful (adj)   /ˈpaʊəfl/
quiet (adj)   /ˈkwaɪət/
rare (adj)   /reə(r)/
relax (v)   /rɪˈlæks/
review (n)   /rɪˈvjuː/
safe (adj)   /seɪf/
start (v)   /stɑːt/
tidy your room (v)   /ˌtaɪdi jɔː ˈruːm/
unhealthy (adj)   /ʌnˈhelθi/
useful (adj)   /ˈjuːsfl/
useless (adj)   /ˈjuːsləs/
wait (v)   /weɪt/
wake up (v)   /ˌweɪk ˈʌp/
watch TV (v)   /ˌwɒtʃ ˌtiː ˈviː/
weak (adj)   /wiːk/

Unit 1

abandoned (adj)   /əˈbændənd/
advert (n)   /ˈædvɜːt/
amusing (adj)   /əˈmjuːzɪŋ/
attract (v)   /əˈtrækt/
audience (n)   /ˈɔːdiəns/
audition (n)   /ɔːˈdɪʃn/
audition (v)   /ɔːˈdɪʃn/
break down (v)   /ˌbreɪk ˈdaʊn/
broadcast (n)   /ˈbrɔːdkɑːst/
broadcast (v)   /ˈbrɔːdkɑːst/
calmly (adv)   /ˈkɑːmli/

camera (n)   /ˈkæmərə/
cartoon (n)   /kɑːˈtuːn/
character (n)   /ˈkærəktə(r)/
chat show (n)   /ˈtʃæt ˌʃəʊ/
choose (v)   /tʃuːz/
cruel (adj)   /ˈkruːəl/
cry (v)   /kraɪ/
debate (n)   /dɪˈbeɪt/
dramatic (adj)   /drəˈmætɪk/
embarrassing (adj)   /ɪmˈbærəsɪŋ/
engineer (n)   /ˌendʒɪˈnɪə(r)/
enjoy (v)   /ɪnˈdʒɔɪ/
entertaining (adj)   /ˌentəˈteɪnɪŋ/
film (n)   /fɪlm/
finally (adv)   /ˈfaɪnəli/
follow (v)   /ˈfɒləʊ/
funny (adj)   /ˈfʌni/
game show (n)   /ˈgeɪm ˌʃəʊ/
leave (v)   /liːv/
lonely (adj)   /ˈləʊnli/
love (v)   /lʌv/
medical drama (n)   /ˈmedɪkl ˌdrɑːmə/
news (n)   /njuːz/
participant (n)   /pɑːˈtɪsɪpənt/
presenter (n)   /prɪˈzentə(r)/
profit (n)   /ˈprɒfɪt/
programme (n)   /ˈprəʊgræm/
quiz show (n)   /ˈkwɪz ˌʃəʊ/
reality show (n)   /riˈæləti ˌʃəʊ/
receive (v)   /rɪˈsiːv/
remote control (n)   /rɪˌməʊt kənˈtrəʊl/
scene (n)   /siːn/
series (n)   /ˈsɪəriːz/
shocked (adj)   /ʃɒkt/
show (n)   /ʃəʊ/
show (v)   /ʃəʊ/
sitcom (n)   /ˈsɪtkɒm/
soap opera (n)   /ˈsəʊp ˌɒprə/
solve (v)   /sɒlv/
sports programme (n)   /ˈspɔːts ˌprəʊgræm/
stuck (adj)   /stʌk/
take part (v)   /ˌteɪk ˈpɑːt/
talent show (n)   /ˈtælənt ˌʃəʊ/
time limit (n)   /ˈtaɪm ˌlɪmɪt/
toilet (n)   /ˈtɔɪlət/
transfer (v)   /trænsˈfɜː(r)/
try (v)   /traɪ/
TV channel (n)   /ˌtiː ˈviː ˌtʃænl/
TV programme (n)   /ˌtiː ˈviː ˌprəʊgræm/
unhappy (adj)   /ʌnˈhæpi/
viewer (n)   /ˈvjuːə(r)/
weather forecast (n)   /ˈweðə ˌfɔːkɑːst/
win (v)   /wɪn/

Unit 2

apple (n)   /ˈæpl/
bag (n)   /bæg/
bar (n)   /bɑː(r)/
barbecue (n)   /ˈbɑːbɪkjuː/
basket (n)   /ˈbɑːskɪt/
beach (n)   /biːtʃ/
blog (n)   /blɒg/
bottle (n)   /ˈbɒtl/
bottle top (n)   /ˈbɒtl ˌtɒp/
box (n)   /bɒks/
burger (n)   /ˈbɜːgə(r)/
burn (v)   /bɜːn/
camerawoman (n)   /ˈkæmərəwʊmən/
can (n)   /kæn/
carton (n)   /ˈkɑːtn/
chicken (n)   /ˈtʃɪkɪn/
chocolate (n)   /ˈtʃɒklət/
Christmas (n)   /ˈkrɪsməs/
cloth (n)   /klɒθ/
coffee (n)   /ˈkɒfi/
computer (n)   /kəmˈpjuːtə(r)/
container (n)   /kənˈteɪnə(r)/
cooking oil (n)   /ˈkʊkɪŋ ˌɔɪl/
crisp (n)   /krɪsp/
cup (n)   /kʌp/
destroy (v)   /dɪˈstrɔɪ/
dishwasher (n)   /ˈdɪʃwɒʃə(r)/
environment (n)   /ɪnˈvaɪrənmənt/
exotic (adj)   /ɪgˈzɒtɪk/
experiment (n)   /ɪkˈsperɪmənt/
fizzy drink (n)   /ˌfɪzi ˈdrɪŋk/
flower (n)   /ˈflaʊə(r)/
fridge (n)   /frɪdʒ/
fuel (n)   /ˈfjuːəl/
harmful (adj)   /ˈhɑːmfl/
ice (n)   /aɪs/

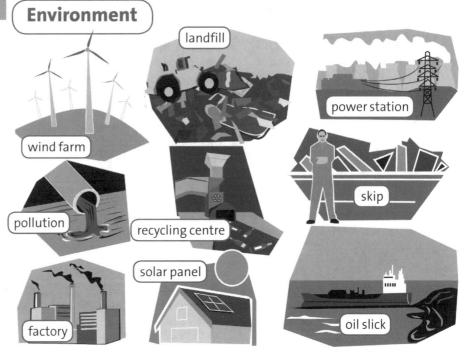

Environment

wind farm
pollution
factory
landfill
recycling centre
solar panel
power station
skip
oil slick

impact (n)   /ˈɪmpækt/
jar (n)   /dʒɑː(r)/
juice (n)   /dʒuːs/
kitchen (n)   /ˈkɪtʃɪn/
kiwi fruit (n)   /ˈkiːwiː ˌfruːt/
lemon (n)   /ˈlemən/
life jacket (n)   /ˈlaɪf ˌdʒækɪt/
lifestyle (n)   /ˈlaɪfstaɪl/
light bulb (n)   /ˈlaɪt ˌbʌlb/
lorry (n)   /ˈlɒri/
mammal (n)   /ˈmæml/
map (n)   /mæp/
match (n)   /mætʃ/
nappy (n)   /ˈnæpi/
newspaper (n)   /ˈnjuːzpeɪpə(r)/
orange (n)   /ˈɒrɪndʒ/

origin (n)   /ˈɒrɪdʒɪn/
packet (n)   /ˈpækɪt/
patrol (v)   /pəˈtrəʊl/
poison (v)   /ˈpɔɪzn/
pollute (v)   /pəˈluːt/
polystyrene (n)   /ˌpɒliˈstaɪriːn/
powder (n)   /ˈpaʊdə(r)/
producer (n)   /prəˈdjuːsə(r)/
recycle (v)   /riːˈsaɪkl/
reduce (v)   /rɪˈdjuːs/
reuse (v)   /riːˈjuːz/
roll (n)   /rəʊl/
rubbish (n)   /ˈrʌbɪʃ/
sandwich (n)   /ˈsænwɪtʃ/
save (v)   /seɪv/
second-hand (adj)   /ˌsekənd ˈhænd/
shampoo (n)   /ʃæmˈpuː/
shopping (n)   /ˈʃɒpɪŋ/
sign (n)   /saɪn/
sleeping bag (n)   /ˈsliːpɪŋ ˌbæg/
soap (n)   /səʊp/
strawberry (n)   /ˈstrɔːbəri/
sugar (n)   /ˈʃʊgə(r)/
sun cream (n)   /ˈsʌn ˌkriːm/
sun hat (n)   /ˈsʌn ˌhæt/
takeaway (adj)   /ˈteɪkəweɪ/
throw away (v)   /ˌθrəʊ əˈweɪ/
toilet paper (n)   /ˈtɔɪlət ˌpeɪpə(r)/
toothpaste (n)   /ˈtuːθpeɪst/
torch (n)   /tɔːtʃ/
tourist (n)   /ˈtʊərɪst/
tube (n)   /tjuːb/
unbelievable (adj)   /ˌʌnbɪˈliːvəbl/
used (adj)   /juːzd/
washing (n)   /ˈwɒʃɪŋ/

Containers

bowl
plate
saucer
glass
mug
jar
jug
carton
can
box
tub
crate
packet

washing machine (n)   /ˈwɒʃɪŋ
   məˌʃiːn/
waste (v, n)   /weɪst/
whale (n)   /weɪl/
wildlife (n)   /ˈwaɪldlaɪf/
yoghurt (n)   /ˈjɒɡət/

Unit 3

addiction (n)   /əˈdɪkʃn/
addictive (adj)   /əˈdɪktɪv/
advice (n)   /ədˈvaɪs/
anti-virus software
   (n)   /ˌænti ˈvaɪrəs ˌsɒftweə(r)/
anywhere (adv)   /ˈeniweə(r)/
appear (v)   /əˈpɪə(r)/
attachment (n)   /əˈtætʃmənt/
avatar (n)   /ˈævətɑː(r)/
back-up copy (n)   /ˈbækʌp ˌkɒpi/
battle (n)   /ˈbætl/
behaviour (n)   /bɪˈheɪvjə(r)/
blog (v)   /blɒɡ/
BMX (n)   /ˌbiː em ˈeks/
buy (v)   /baɪ/
career (n)   /kəˈrɪə(r)/
careful (adj)   /ˈkeəfl/
chat (v)   /tʃæt/
chat room (n)   /ˈtʃæt ˌruːm/
clinic (n)   /ˈklɪnɪk/
clothes (n)   /kləʊðz/
comment (n)   /ˈkɒment/
communicate (v)   /kəˈmjuːnɪkeɪt/
community (n)   /kəˈmjuːnəti/
compare (v)   /kəmˈpeə(r)/
connect (v)   /kəˈnekt/
cool (adj)   /kuːl/
crash (v)   /kræʃ/
cure (n)   /kjʊə(r)/

depressed (adj)   /dɪˈprest/
design (v)   /dɪˈzaɪn/
disconnect (v)   /dɪskəˈnekt/
download (v)   /daʊnˈləʊd/
download (n)   /ˈdaʊnləʊd/
eat (v)   /iːt/
education (n)   /edʒuˈkeɪʃn/
email (v)   /ˈiːmeɪl/
email (n)   /ˈiːmeɪl/
experience (n)   /ɪkˈspɪəriəns/
fail (v)   /feɪl/
fight (v)   /faɪt/
file (n)   /faɪl/
file sharing (n)   /ˈfaɪl ˌʃeərɪŋ/
find (v)   /faɪnd/
firewall (n)   /ˈfaɪəwɔːl/
freestyle (adj)   /ˈfriːstaɪl/
furniture (n)   /ˈfɜːnɪtʃə(r)/
gamer (n)   /ˈɡeɪmə(r)/
habit (n)   /ˈhæbɪt/
hacker (n)   /ˈhækə(r)/
identity (n)   /aɪˈdentəti/
inbox (n)   /ˈɪnbɒks/
instant messaging (IM) (n)
   /ˌɪnstənt ˈmesɪdʒɪŋ/
isolated (adj)   /ˈaɪsəleɪtɪd/
join (v)   /dʒɔɪn/
message (v)   /ˈmesɪdʒ/
message board (n)   /ˈmesɪdʒ ˌbɔːd/
mobile (n)   /ˈməʊbaɪl/
moderator (n)   /ˈmɒdəreɪtə(r)/
money (n)   /ˈmʌni/
obsessive (adj)   /əbˈsesɪv/
offline (adj)   /ɒfˈlaɪn/
ogre (n)   /ˈəʊɡə(r)/
online (adj)   /ɒnˈlaɪn/
password (n)   /ˈpɑːswɜːd/

personal webpage (n)   /ˌpɜːsənl
   ˈwebpeɪdʒ/
phishing (n)   /ˈfɪʃɪŋ/
place (n)   /pleɪs/
popular (adj)   /ˈpɒpjələ(r)/
post a message (v)   /ˌpəʊst ə
   ˈmesɪdʒ/
psychologist (n)   /saɪˈkɒlədʒɪst/
put (v)   /pʊt/
ramp (n)   /ræmp/
relationship (n)   /rɪˈleɪʃnʃɪp/
report (v)   /rɪˈpɔːt/
ride (v)   /raɪd/
ruin (v)   /ˈruːɪn/
search (v)   /sɜːtʃ/
search engine (n)   /ˈsɜːtʃ ˌendʒɪn/
sell (v)   /sel/
sensibly (adv)   /ˈsensəbli/
serious (adj)   /ˈsɪəriəs/
share (v)   /ʃeə(r)/
skatepark (n)   /ˈskeɪtpɑːk/
sleep (v)   /sliːp/
spam (n)   /spæm/
spam filter (n)   /ˈspæm ˌfɪltə(r)/
speak (v)   /spiːk/
spend (v)   /spend/
stay up (v)   /ˌsteɪ ˈʌp/
stolen (adj)   /ˈstəʊlən/
symptom (n)   /ˈsɪmptəm/
time-consuming (adj)   /ˈtaɪm
   kənˌsjuːmɪŋ/
track (n)   /træk/
trick (n)   /trɪk/
type (n)   /taɪp/
urban (adj)   /ˈɜːbən/
virtual (adj)   /ˈvɜːtʃuəl/
virus (n)   /ˈvaɪrəs/
visit (v)   /ˈvɪzɪt/
webcam (n)   /ˈwebkæm/
write (v)   /raɪt/

Gadgets and household items

plug
torch
scissors
battery
key
light bulb
tap
fan
USB
key ring
wire
lock
cable
calculator
recharger
candle

Unit 4

academic (adj)   /ækəˈdemɪk/
accept (v)   /əkˈsept/
active (adj)   /ˈæktɪv/
adventurous (adj)   /ədˈventʃərəs/
advertise (v)   /ˈædvətaɪz/
ambitious (adj)   /æmˈbɪʃəs/
art (n)   /ɑːt/
astronaut (n)   /ˈæstrənɔːt/
attention (n)   /əˈtenʃn/
benefit (v)   /ˈbenəfɪt/
break (n)   /breɪk/
cheerful (adj)   /ˈtʃɪəfl/
confident (adj)   /ˈkɒnfɪdənt/
courage (n)   /ˈkʌrɪdʒ/
courageous (adj)   /kəˈreɪdʒəs/
creative (adj)   /kriˈeɪtɪv/

creativity (n)   /krieɪˈtɪvəti/
critical (adj)   /ˈkrɪtɪkl/
curious (adj)   /ˈkjʊəriəs/
curved (adj)   /kɜːvd/
dead end (n)   /ˌded ˈend/
determined (adj)   /dɪˈtɜːmɪnd/
drama (n)   /ˈdrɑːmə/
early (adv)   /ˈɜːli/
ego (n)   /ˈiːɡəʊ/
egotistical (adj)   /eɡəˈtɪstɪkl, iːɡə-/
entertainment (n)   /entəˈteɪnmənt/
eyebrow (n)   /ˈaɪbraʊ/
fair (adj)   /feə(r)/
fame (n)   /feɪm/
famous (adj)   /ˈfeɪməs/
friendly (adj)   /ˈfrendli/
generous (adj)   /ˈdʒenərəs/
give up (v)   /ˌɡɪv ˈʌp/
good-looking (adj)   /ˌɡʊd ˈlʊkɪŋ/
gossip magazine (n)   /ˈɡɒsɪp
  ˌmæɡəˌziːn/
hit (n)   /hɪt/
hopeful (adj)   /ˈhəʊpfl/
incredibly (adv)   /ɪnˈkredəbli/
independence (n)   /ɪndɪˈpendəns/
independent (adj)   /ɪndɪˈpendənt/
innocent (adj)   /ˈɪnəsnt/
intelligence (n)   /ɪnˈtelɪdʒəns/

intelligent (adj)   /ɪnˈtelɪdʒənt/
intolerant (adj)   /ɪnˈtɒlərənt/
involved (adj)   /ɪnˈvɒlvd/
large (adj)   /lɑːdʒ/
luck (n)   /lʌk/
lucky (adj)   /ˈlʌki/
mean (adj)   /miːn/
media (n)   /ˈmiːdiə/
media studies (n)   /ˈmiːdiə ˌstʌdiz/
one-hit wonder (n)   /ˌwʌn ˌhɪt
  ˈwʌndə(r)/
opportunity (n)   /ɒpəˈtjuːnəti/
oval (adj)   /ˈəʊvl/
overnight (adj)   /əʊvəˈnaɪt/
plan (n)   /plæn/
practical (adj)   /ˈpræktɪkl/
profitable (adj)   /ˈprɒfɪtəbl/
public eye (n)   /ˌpʌblɪk ˈaɪ/
really (adv)   /ˈriːəli/
role model (n)   /ˈrəʊl ˌmɒdl/
round (adj)   /raʊnd/
sensation (n)   /senˈseɪʃn/
sensible (adj)   /ˈsensəbl/
sensitive (adj)   /ˈsensətɪv/
shy (adj)   /ʃaɪ/
skilful (adj)   /ˈskɪlfl/
skill (n)   /skɪl/
soundtrack (n)   /ˈsaʊndtræk/

square (adj)   /skweə(r)/
straight (adj)   /streɪt/
strength (n)   /streŋθ/
strong (adj)   /strɒŋ/
stylish (adj)   /ˈstaɪlɪʃ/
successful (adj)   /səkˈsesfl/
summary (n)   /ˈsʌməri/
survey (n)   /ˈsɜːveɪ/
talent (n)   /ˈtælənt/
talented (adj)   /ˈtæləntɪd/
tend (v)   /tend/
tolerant (adj)   /ˈtɒlərənt/
unique (adj)   /juˈniːk/
wannabe (adj)   /ˈwɒnəbi/
wide (adj)   /waɪd/

Unit 5

absent (adj)   /ˈæbsənt/
against (prep)   /əˈɡenst/
aspect (n)   /ˈæspekt/
attitude (n)   /ˈætɪtjuːd/
ban (v)   /bæn/
beat (v)   /biːt/
biscuit (n)   /ˈbɪskɪt/
bully (v)   /ˈbʊli/
calculator (n)   /ˈkælkjəleɪtə(r)/
candy (n) (NAME)   /ˈkændi/

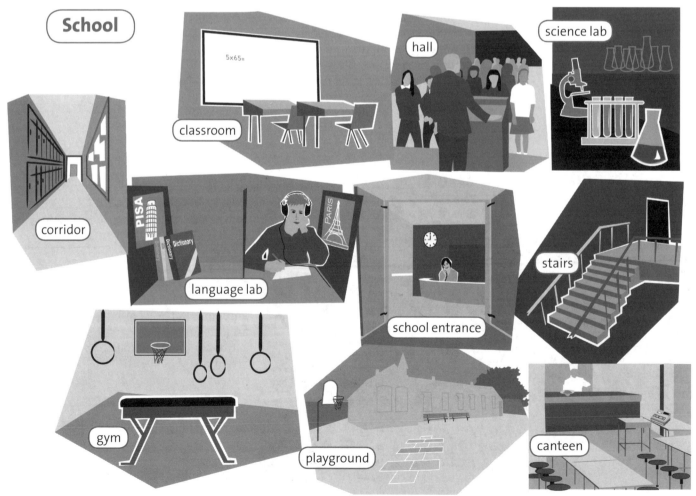

School

classroom

hall

science lab

corridor

language lab

school entrance

stairs

gym

playground

canteen

canteen (n)   /kæn'ti:n/
cell phone (n) (NAME)   /'sel ˌfəʊn/
cheat (n)   /tʃi:t/
cheat (v)   /tʃi:t/
chewing gum (n)   /'tʃu:ɪŋ ˌgʌm/
classroom (n)   /'klɑ:sru:m/
clever (adj)   /'klevə(r)/
compulsory (adj)   /kəm'pʌlsəri/
conclusion (n)   /kən'klu:ʒn/
convenient (adj)   /kən'vi:niənt/
cookie (n)   /'kʊki/
copy (v)   /'kɒpi/
corridor (n)   /'kɒrɪdɔ:(r)/
definitely (adv)   /'defɪnətli/
detect (v)   /dɪ'tekt/
essay (n)   /'eseɪ/
exam (n)   /ɪg'zæm/
expel (v)   /ɪk'spel/
firstly (adv)   /'fɜ:stli/
foreign (adj)   /'fɒrən/
freeway (n) (NAME)   /'fri:weɪ/
gasoline (n) (NAME)   /'gæsəli:n/
grade (n)   /greɪd/
gym (n)   /dʒɪm/
head teacher (n)   /ˌhed 'ti:tʃə(r)/
high school (n)   /'haɪ ˌsku:l/
history (n)   /'hɪstri/
homework (n)   /'həʊmwɜ:k/
ideal (adj)   /aɪ'di:əl/
in favour of (adj)   /ˌɪn 'feɪvər əv/
interview (v)   /'ɪntəvju:/
leave school (v)   /ˌli:v 'sku:l/
legal (adj)   /'li:gl/
library (n)   /'laɪbrəri/
lie (v)   /laɪ/
make friends (v)   /ˌmeɪk 'frendz/
mark (n)   /mɑ:k/
maths (n)   /mæθs/
mixed (adj)   /mɪkst/
motorway (n)   /'məʊtəweɪ/
movie (n) (NAME)   /'mu:vi/
mp3 player (n)   /ˌem ˌpi: 'θri: ˌpleɪə(r)/
nasty (adj)   /'nɑ:sti/
national anthem (n)   /ˌnæʃnəl 'ænθəm/
pants (n) (NAME)   /pænts/
pass (an exam) (v)   /ˌpɑ:s (ən ɪg'zæm)/
pavement (n)   /'peɪvmənt/
petrol (n)   /'petrəl/
play truant (v)   /ˌpleɪ 'tru:ənt/
policy (n)   /'pɒləsi/
pressure (n)   /'preʃə(r)/
primary school (n)   /'praɪməri ˌsku:l/
principal (n)   /'prɪnsəpl/
private school (n)   /'praɪvət ˌsku:l/

qualification (n)   /ˌkwɒlɪfɪ'keɪʃn/
revise (v)   /rɪ'vaɪz/
rule (n)   /ru:l/
school yard (n)   /'sku:l ˌjɑ:d/
science (n)   /'saɪəns/
secondary school (n)   /'sekəndri ˌsku:l/
secondly (adv)   /'sekəndli/
set an example (v)   /ˌset ən ɪg'zɑ:mpl/
shop (n)   /ʃɒp/
shoulder (n)   /'ʃəʊldə(r)/
sidewalk (n) (NAME)   /'saɪdwɔ:k/
single-sex (adj)   /'sɪŋgl ˌseks/
state school (n)   /'steɪt ˌsku:l/
store (n) (NAME)   /stɔ:(r)/
subject (n)   /'sʌbdʒɪkt/
succeed (v)   /sək'si:d/
summarize (v)   /'sʌməraɪz/
suspend (v)   /sə'spend/
sweet (n)   /swi:t/
take (an exam) (v)   /ˌteɪk (ən ɪg'zæm)/
test (n)   /test/
text message (n)   /'tekst ˌmesɪdʒ/
trash (n) (NAME)   /træʃ/
trousers (n)   /'traʊzəz/
truck (n) (NAME)   /trʌk/
understand (v)   /ʌndə'stænd/
unfortunately (adv)   /ʌn'fɔ:tʃənətli/
uniform (n)   /'ju:nɪfɔ:m/
upset (adj)   /ʌp'set/
wear (v)   /weə(r)/
winner (n)   /'wɪnə(r)/
worry (v)   /'wʌri/

wrong (adj)   /rɒŋ/

Unit 6

abroad (adv)   /ə'brɔ:d/
alternative (n)   /ɔ:l'tɜ:nətɪv, ɒlt-/
ban (n)   /bæn/
billion (n)   /'bɪljən/
boycott (n)   /'bɔɪkɒt/
boycott (v)   /'bɔɪkɒt/
building (n)   /'bɪldɪŋ/
campaign (n)   /kæm'peɪn/
campaign (v)   /kæm'peɪn/
carry on (v)   /ˌkæri 'ɒn/
cause (n)   /kɔ:z/
chain (n)   /tʃeɪn/
charity (n)   /'tʃærəti/
collect (v)   /kə'lekt/
collection (n)   /kə'lekʃn/
coordinator (n)   /kəʊ'ɔ:dɪneɪtə(r)/
distribute (v)   /dɪ'strɪbju:t, 'dɪst-/
donate (v)   /dəʊ'neɪt/
donation (n)   /dəʊ'neɪʃn/
draw attention to (v)   /ˌdrɔ: ə'tenʃn tə/
end up (v)   /ˌend 'ʌp/
faithfully (adv)   /'feɪθfəli/
find out (v)   /ˌfaɪnd 'aʊt/
forever (adv)   /fər'evə(r)/
freegan (n)   /'fri:gən/
government (n)   /'gʌvnmənt/
handout (n)   /'hændaʊt/
hungry (adj)   /'hʌŋgri/
impatient (adj)   /ɪm'peɪʃnt/
important (adj)   /ɪm'pɔ:tnt/

Protest

placard
banner
megaphone
sticker
cordon
barrier
leaflet

impractical (adj)   /ɪmˈpræktɪkl/
insane (adj)   /ɪnˈseɪn/
insensitive (adj)   /ɪnˈsensətɪv/
join in (v)   /ˌdʒɔɪn ˈɪn/
journalist (n)   /ˈdʒɜːnəlɪst/
kill (v)   /kɪl/
leaflet (n)   /ˈliːflət/
lifetime (n)   /ˈlaɪftaɪm/
look after (v)   /ˌlʊk ˈɑːftə(r)/
magnificent (adj)   /mægˈnɪfɪsnt/
marathon (n)   /ˈmærəθən/
march (n)   /mɑːtʃ/
march (v)   /mɑːtʃ/
meat (n)   /miːt/
meet (v)   /miːt/
meeting (n)   /ˈmiːtɪŋ/
newsletter (n)   /ˈnjuːzletə(r)/
nuclear power station (n)
   /ˌnjuːkliə ˈpaʊə ˌsteɪʃn/
occur (v)   /əˈkɜː(r)/
organization (n)   /ɔːgənaɪˈzeɪʃn/
organize (v)   /ˈɔːgənaɪz/
participate (v)   /pɑːˈtɪsɪpeɪt/
petition (n)   /pəˈtɪʃn/
petition (v)   /pəˈtɪʃn/
poor (adj)   /pɔː(r)/
protest (n)   /ˈprəʊtest/
protest (v)   /prəˈtest/
publicity (n)   /pʌbˈlɪsəti/

publicize (v)   /ˈpʌblɪsaɪz/
renewable (adj)   /rɪˈnjuːəbl/
represent (v)   /reprɪˈzent/
set up (v)   /ˌset ˈʌp/
sign up (v)   /ˌsaɪn ˈʌp/
size (n)   /saɪz/
species (n)   /ˈspiːʃiːz/
sponsor (v)   /ˈspɒnsə(r)/
strict (adj)   /strɪkt/
subscribe (v)   /səbˈskraɪb/
support (n)   /səˈpɔːt/
support (v)   /səˈpɔːt/
third (n)   /θɜːd/
unacceptable (adj)   /ʌnəkˈseptəbl/
unkind (adj)   /ʌnˈkaɪnd/
unnecessary (adj)   /ʌnˈnesəsəri/
violent (adj)   /ˈvaɪələnt/
voluntary (adj)   /ˈvɒləntri/
volunteer (n)   /vɒlənˈtɪə(r)/
volunteer (v)   /vɒlənˈtɪə(r)/
waste (n)   /weɪst/
waste bin (n)   /ˈweɪst ˌbɪn/
wipe out (v)   /ˌwaɪp ˈaʊt/

Unit 7

act (v)   /ækt/
adventure (n)   /ədˈventʃə(r)/
alien (n)   /ˈeɪliən/
alone (adj)   /əˈləʊn/
animation (n)   /æniˈmeɪʃn/
appeal (v)   /əˈpiːl/
archery (n)   /ˈɑːtʃəri/
attack (v)   /əˈtæk/
best-seller (n)   /ˌbest ˈselə(r)/
biography (n)   /baɪˈɒgrəfi/
blockbuster (n)   /ˈblɒkbʌstə(r)/
body (n)   /ˈbɒdi/
brain (n)   /breɪn/
cast (n)   /kɑːst/
classic (adj)   /ˈklæsɪk/
clear (adj)   /klɪə(r)/
comedy (n)   /ˈkɒmədi/
concentration camp (n)
   /kɒnsənˈtreɪʃn ˌkæmp/
conduct (v)   /kənˈdʌkt/
conductor (n)   /kənˈdʌktə(r)/
crazy (adj)   /ˈkreɪzi/
creature (n)   /ˈkriːtʃə(r)/
darkness (n)   /ˈdɑːknəs/
day dreamer (n)   /ˈdeɪ ˌdriːmə(r)/
dead (adj)   /ded/
deal (n)   /diːl/

Cinema

queue
CINEMA
projector
usher
poster
Meet the RELATIVES

foyer
aisle
3D glasses

audience
ticket office
screen

delight (v)   /dɪ'laɪt/
detective (n)   /dɪ'tektɪv/
dialogue (n)   /'daɪəlɒg/
digital projector (n)   /ˌdɪdʒɪtl prə'dʒektə(r)/
direct (v)   /də'rekt, dɪ-, daɪ-/
director (n)   /də'rektə(r), dɪ-, daɪ-/
DVD (n)   /ˌdiː ˌviː 'diː/
emotion (n)   /ɪ'məʊʃn/
ending (n)   /'endɪŋ/
epic (adj)   /'epɪk/
everywhere (adv)   /'evriweə(r)/
express (v)   /ɪk'spres/
fact (n)   /fækt/
fantasy (n)   /'fæntəsi/
friendship (n)   /'frendʃɪp/
genre (n)   /'ʒɒnrə/
greedy (adj)   /'griːdi/
hate (v)   /heɪt/
hear (v)   /hɪə(r)/
horror (n)   /'hɒrə(r)/
horse riding (n)   /'hɔːs ˌraɪdɪŋ/
imagination (n)   /ɪˌmædʒɪ'neɪʃn/
impact (n)   /'ɪmpækt/
improve (v)   /ɪm'pruːv/
invent (v)   /ɪn'vent/
inventor (n)   /ɪn'ventə(r)/
martial arts (n)   /ˌmɑːʃl 'ɑːts/
memorable (adj)   /'memərəbl/
mess (n)   /mes/
messy (adj)   /'mesi/
mind (v)   /maɪnd/
musical (n)   /'mjuːzɪkl/
mystery (n)   /'mɪstri/
narrate (v)   /nə'reɪt/
novelist (n)   /'nɒvəlɪst/
opinion (n)   /ə'pɪnjən/
paint (v)   /peɪnt/
painter (n)   /'peɪntə(r)/
paragraph (n)   /'pærəgrɑːf/
particularly (adv)   /pə'tɪkjələli/
permanent (adj)   /'pɜːmənənt/
pianist (n)   /'pɪənɪst/
plot (n)   /plɒt/
podcast (n)   /'pɒdkɑːst/
prefer (v)   /prɪ'fɜː(r)/
provide (v)   /prə'vaɪd/
publisher (n)   /'pʌblɪʃə(r)/
quality (n)   /'kwɒləti/
realism (n)   /'riːəlɪzəm/
realistic (adj)   /riːə'lɪstɪk/
recommend (v)   /rekə'mend/
remake (n)   /'riːmeɪk/
replace (v)   /rɪ'pleɪs/
revolutionize (v)   /revə'luːʃənaɪz/
role (n)   /rəʊl/
romance (n)   /rəʊ'mæns/
scent (n)   /sent/

science fiction (n)   /ˌsaɪəns 'fɪkʃn/
screen (n)   /skriːn/
setting (n)   /'setɪŋ/
shower (n)   /'ʃaʊə(r)/
silent movie (n)   /'saɪlənt ˌmuːvi/
simple (adj)   /'sɪmpl/
smell (n)   /smel/
smell (v)   /smel/
space (n)   /speɪs/
speaker (n)   /'spiːkə(r)/
special effects (n pl)   /ˌspeʃl ɪ'fekts/
spy (n)   /spaɪ/
star (v)   /stɑː(r)/
statement (n)   /'steɪtmənt/
stimulate (v)   /'stɪmjuleɪt/
story (n)   /'stɔːri/
subtitles (n)   /'sʌbtaɪtlz/
surround sound (n)   /sə'raʊnd ˌsaʊnd/
theme (n)   /θiːm/
thriller (n)   /'θrɪlə(r)/
tidy (adj)   /'taɪdi/
title (n)   /'taɪtl/
translate (v)   /træns'leɪt/
translator (n)   /træns'leɪtə(r)/
trilogy (n)   /'trɪlədʒi/
unusual (adj)   /ʌn'juːʒuəl/
value (v)   /'væljuː/
various (adj)   /'veəriəs/
voice (n)   /vɔɪs/
war (n)   /wɔː(r)/
western (n)   /'westən/

Landscape

in the top left-hand corner   at the top   in the distance
in the background
on the left   in the middle   on the right
in the foreground
at the bottom   in the bottom right-hand corner

Unit 8

abstract (adj)   /'æbstrækt/
actually (adv)   /'æktʃuəli/
adore (v)   /ə'dɔː(r)/
amuse (v)   /ə'mjuːz/
art movement (n)   /'ɑːt ˌmuːvmənt/
attractive (adj)   /ə'træktɪv/
auction (n)   /'ɔːkʃn/
background (n)   /'bækgraʊnd/
bizarre (adj)   /bɪ'zɑː(r)/
bright (adj)   /braɪt/
bronze (n)   /brɒnz/
cliff (n)   /klɪf/
collector (n)   /kə'lektə(r)/
colourful (adj)   /'kʌləfl/
composition (n)   /kɒmpə'zɪʃn/
conceptual (adj)   /kən'septʃuəl/
conservative (adj)   /kən'sɜːvətɪv/
controversial (adj)   /kɒntrə'vɜːʃl/
critic (n)   /'krɪtɪk/
criticize (v)   /'krɪtɪsaɪz/
dark (adj)   /dɑːk/
destructive (adj)   /dɪ'strʌktɪv/
dream (n)   /driːm/
dull (adj)   /dʌl/
everyday (adj)   /'evrideɪ/
exhibition (n)   /eksɪ'bɪʃn/
foreground (n)   /'fɔːgraʊnd/
fun (adj)   /fʌn/
gallery (n)   /'gæləri/
gold (n)   /gəʊld/
image (n)   /'ɪmɪdʒ/
imaginative (adj)   /ɪ'mædʒɪnətɪv/
include (v)   /ɪn'kluːd/
indifferent (adj)   /ɪn'dɪfrənt/

influential (adj) /ˌɪnfluˈenʃl/
inform (v) /ɪnˈfɔːm/
inspire (v) /ɪnˈspaɪə(r)/
intense (adj) /ɪnˈtens/
landscape (n) /ˈlændskeɪp/
liquid (n) /ˈlɪkwɪd/
mad (adj) /mæd/
marble (n) /ˈmɑːbl/
masterpiece (n) /ˈmɑːstəpiːs/
melt (v) /melt/
modern (adj) /ˈmɒdn/
museum (n) /mjuˈziːəm/
negative (adj) /ˈnegətɪv/
oil painting (n) /ˈɔɪl ˌpeɪntɪŋ/
original (adj) /əˈrɪdʒənl/
painting (n) /ˈpeɪntɪŋ/
portrait (n) /ˈpɔːtreɪt/
provocative (adj) /prəˈvɒkətɪv/
reject (v) /rɪˈdʒekt/
remind (v) /rɪˈmaɪnd/
ridiculous (adj) /rɪˈdɪkjələs/
scenery (n) /ˈsiːnəri/
sculpture (n) /ˈskʌlptʃə(r)/
shed (n) /ʃed/
shocking (adj) /ˈʃɒkɪŋ/
sick (adj) /sɪk/
stool (n) /stuːl/
strange (adj) /streɪndʒ/
surrealism (n) /səˈriːəlɪzəm/
surrealist (n) /səˈriːəlɪst/
traditional (adj) /trəˈdɪʃənl/
watch (n) /wɒtʃ/
weird (adj) /wɪəd/

English Plus Options

Extra listening and speaking

Unit 1
magazine (n) /mægəˈziːn/
sofa (n) /ˈsəʊfə/

Unit 2
aspirin (n) /ˈæsprɪn/
batteries (n) /ˈbætəriz/
deodorant (n) /diˈəʊdərənt/
tube (n) /tjuːb/
washing-up liquid (n)
/ˌwɒʃɪŋ ˌʌp ˌlɪkwɪd/
watt (n) /wɒt/

Unit 3
forward (adj) /ˈfɔːwəd/
hyphen (n) /ˈhaɪfən/
slash (n) /slæʃ/

Unit 4
picture (v) /ˈpɪktʃə(r)/

scarf (n) /skɑːf/

Unit 5
hockey (n) /ˈhɒki/
proper (adj) /ˈprɒpə(r)/

Unit 6
achieve (v) /əˈtʃiːv/
hope (v) /həʊp/
listener (n) /ˈlɪsnə(r)/
placard (n) /ˈplækɑːd/

Unit 7
believable (adj) /bɪˈliːvəbl/
love story (n) /ˈlʌv ˌstɔːri/
romantic (adj) /rəʊˈmæntɪk/
vampire (n) /ˈvæmpaɪə(r)/

Unit 8
countryside (n) /ˈkʌntrisaɪd/
leaf (n) /liːf/
lovely (adj) /ˈlʌvli/
monkey (n) /ˈmʌŋki/
sky (n) /skaɪ/

Curriculum extra

Unit 1
aerial (n) /ˈeəriəl/
analogue (adj) /ˈænəlɒg/
binary code (n) /ˈbaɪnəri ˌkəʊd/
broadcaster (n) /ˈbrɔːdkɑːstə(r)/
cable (n) /ˈkeɪbl/
convert (v) /kənˈvɜːt/
decoder (n) /diːˈkəʊdə(r)/
interference (n) /ˌɪntəˈfɪərəns/
radio wave (n) /ˈreɪdiəʊ ˌweɪv/
revolutionary (adj) /ˌrevəˈluːʃənəri/
satellite dish (n) /ˈsætəlaɪt ˌdɪʃ/
separate (adj) /ˈseprət/
transform (v) /trænsˈfɔːm/

Unit 2
agenda (n) /əˈdʒendə/
collective (adj) /kəˈlektɪv/
facility (n) /fəˈsɪləti/
global (adj) /ˈgləʊbl/
globally (adv) /ˈgləʊbəli/
huge (adj) /hjuːdʒ/
poverty (n) /ˈpɒvəti/
refer (v) /rɪˈfɜː(r)/
responsibility (n) /rɪˌspɒnsəˈbɪləti/
save (v) /seɪv/
solution (n) /səˈluːʃn/
summit (n) /ˈsʌmɪt/

Unit 3
content (n) /ˈkɒntent/
double-check (v) /ˌdʌbl ˈtʃek/
go live (v) /ˌgəʊ ˈlaɪv/
offensive (adj) /əˈfensɪv/

update (v) /ʌpˈdeɪt/
use (v) /juːz/
vandalism (n) /ˈvændəlɪzəm/
wiki (n) /ˈwɪki/

Unit 4
article (n) /ˈɑːtɪkl/
colloquial (adj) /kəˈləʊkwiəl/
complex (adj) /ˈkɒmpleks/
concentrate (v) /ˈkɒnsəntreɪt/
crossword (n) /ˈkrɒswɜːd/
design (n) /dɪˈzaɪn/
disaster (n) /dɪˈzɑːstə(r)/
economics (n) /ˌiːkəˈnɒmɪks, ˌeke-/
headline (n) /ˈhedlaɪn/
horoscope (n) /ˈhɒrəskəʊp/
obituary (n) /əˈbɪtʃuəri/
politics (n) /ˈpɒlətɪks/
sensationalist (adj)
/senˈseɪʃənəlɪst/
technique (n) /tekˈniːk/

Unit 5
antisocial (adj) /ˌænti ˈsəʊʃl/
appropriate (adj) /əˈprəʊpriət/
citizenship (n) /ˈsɪtɪznʃɪp/
deal (v) /diːl/
detention (n) /dɪˈtenʃn/
discipline (n) /ˈdɪsəplɪn/
disrupt (v) /dɪsˈrʌpt/
disruptive (adj) /dɪsˈrʌptɪv/
disturb (v) /dɪˈstɜːb/
emotional (adj) /ɪˈməʊʃənl/
insult (n) /ˈɪnsʌlt/
lack (n) /læk/
miniature (adj) /ˈmɪnətʃə(r)/
physical (adj) /ˈfɪzɪkl/
prevention (n) /prɪˈvenʃn/
punishment (n) /ˈpʌnɪʃmənt/
rumour (n) /ˈruːmə(r)/
spread (v) /spred/
strategy (n) /ˈstrætədʒi/
verbal (adj) /ˈvɜːbl/
violence (n) /ˈvaɪələns/

Unit 6
bird (n) /bɜːd/
canopy (n) /ˈkænəpi/
dense (adj) /dens/
diverse (adj) /daɪˈvɜːs/
emergent (adj) /iˈmɜːdʒənt/
farming (n) /ˈfɑːmɪŋ/
floor (n) /flɔː(r)/
forest (n) /ˈfɒrɪst/
insect (n) /ˈɪnsekt/
jaguar (n) /ˈdʒægjuə(r)/
layer (n) /ˈleɪə(r)/
medicinal (adj) /məˈdɪsɪnl/
natural (adj) /ˈnætʃrəl/
reptile (n) /ˈreptaɪl/

shrub (n) /ʃrʌb/
sustainable (adj) /sə'steɪnəbl/
tapir (n) /'teɪpə(r)/
understory (n) /'ʌndəstɔːri/
vegetation (n) /ˌvedʒə'teɪʃn/
wood (n) /wʊd/

Unit 7

chin (n) /tʃɪn/
conversation (n) /kɒnvə'seɪʃn/
converse (v) /kən'vɜːs/
difference (n) /'dɪfrəns/
different (adj) /'dɪfrənt/
ear (n) /ɪə(r)/
eye (n) /aɪ/
feel (v) /fiːl/
feeling (n) /'fiːlɪŋ/
fool (n) /fuːl/
mean (v) /miːn/
meaning (n) /'miːnɪŋ/
move (v) /muːv/
movement (n) /'muːvmənt/
neck (n) /nek/
pointed (adj) /'pɔɪntɪd/
prettiness (n) /'prɪtinəs/
pretty (adj) /'prɪti/
purple (adj) /'pɜːpl/
sad (adj) /sæd/
sadness (n) /'sædnəs/
sharp (adj) /ʃɑːp/
softly (adv) /'sɒftli/
thunder (n) /'θʌndə(r)/
wavy (adj) /'weɪvi/

Unit 8

bold (adj) /bəʊld/
brand name (n) /'brænd ˌneɪm/
broad (adj) /brɔːd/
brush (n) /brʌʃ/
canvas (n) /'kænvəs/
comic strip (n) /'kɒmɪk ˌstrɪp/
consumerism (n)
  /kən'sjuːmərɪzəm/
depict (v) /dɪ'pɪkt/
drip (n) /drɪp/
drip (v) /drɪp/
expressionism (n)
  /ɪk'spreʃənɪzəm/
force (v) /fɔːs/
freedom (n) /'friːdəm/
materialism (n) /mə'tɪəriəlɪzəm/
packaging (n) /'pækɪdʒɪŋ/
paint (n) /peɪnt/
Pop Art (n) /'pɒp ˌɑːt/
pretentious (adj) /prɪ'tenʃəs/
profound (adj) /prə'faʊnd/

Culture

Unit 1

average (adj) /'ævərɪdʒ/
awareness (n) /ə'weənəs/
detox (n) /'diːtɒks/
dinner (n) /'dɪnə(r)/
encourage (v) /ɪn'kʌrɪdʒ/
entire (adj) /ɪn'taɪə(r)/
mental (adj) /'mentl/
murder (n) /'mɜːdə(r)/
regularly (adv) /'regjələli/
switch off (v) /ˌswɪtʃ 'ɒf/
universal (adj) /juːnɪ'vɜːsl/

Unit 2

beach (n) /biːtʃ/
clear away (v) /ˌklɪər ə'weɪ/
compete (v) /kəm'piːt/
continent (n) /'kɒntɪnənt/
coral (n) /'kɒrəl/
diver (n) /'daɪvə(r)/
park (n) /pɑːk/
plant (v) /plɑːnt/
river bank (n) /'rɪvə ˌbæŋk/
sailor (n) /'seɪlə(r)/
street (n) /striːt/
tree (n) /triː/
underwater (adj) /ˌʌndə'wɔːtə(r)/

Unit 3

arrival (n) /ə'raɪvl/
growth (n) /grəʊθ/
leader (n) /'liːdə(r)/
married (adj) /'mærid/
microblogging (n)
  /'maɪkrəʊblɒgɪŋ/
networking (n) /'netwɜːkɪŋ/
overall (adj) /ˌəʊvər'ɔːl/
rich (adj) /rɪtʃ/
statistic (n) /stə'tɪstɪk/
unknown (adj) /ˌʌn'nəʊn/
whole (adj) /həʊl/

Unit 4

album (n) /'ælbəm/
audio clip (n) /'ɔːdiəʊ ˌklɪp/
championship (n) /'tʃæmpiənʃɪp/
concert (n) /'kɒnsət/
copy (n) /'kɒpi/
cover (n) /'kʌvə(r)/
designer (adj) /dɪ'zaɪnə(r)/
feature (n) /'fiːtʃə(r)/
fitness (n) /'fɪtnəs/
Formula 1 (n) /ˌfɔːmjələ 'wʌn/
jewellery (n) /'dʒuːəlri/
make-up (n) /'meɪk ˌʌp/
personality (n) /pɜːsə'næləti/
quiz (n) /kwɪz/
similar (adj) /'sɪmələ(r)/
value (n) /'væljuː/

Unit 5

beautiful (adj) /'bjuːtɪfl/
brilliant (adj) /'brɪliənt/
caring (adj) /'keərɪŋ/
co-educational (adj)
  /ˌkəʊ edʒu'keɪʃənl/
destination (n) /destɪ'neɪʃn/
disappointed (adj) /dɪsə'pɔɪntɪd/
discussion (n) /dɪs'kʌʃn/
film studies (n) /'fɪlm ˌstʌdiz/
free-thinking (adj) /ˌfriː 'θɪŋkɪŋ/
homesick (adj) /'həʊmsɪk/
kind (adj) /kaɪnd/
mountaineering (n)
  /maʊntə'nɪərɪŋ/
obvious (adj) /'ɒbviəs/
relaxed (adj) /rɪ'lækst/
rugby (n) /'rʌgbi/
sailing (n) /'seɪlɪŋ/
standard (n) /'stændəd/
stimulating (adj) /'stɪmjuleɪtɪŋ/
stressful (adj) /'stresfl/

Unit 6

baked beans (n) /ˌbeɪkt 'biːnz/
bath (n) /bɑːθ/
celebrity (n) /sə'lebrəti/
comedian (n) /kə'miːdiən/
disease (n) /dɪ'ziːz/
hairstyle (n) /'heəstaɪl/
hunger (n) /'hʌngə(r)/
injustice (n) /ɪn'dʒʌstɪs/
last (v) /lɑːst/
project (n) /'prɒdʒekt/
raise (v) /reɪz/
sketch (n) /sketʃ/
sportsperson (n) /'spɔːtspɜːsn/

Unit 7

combination (n) /kɒmbɪ'neɪʃn/
continue (v) /kən'tɪnjuː/
explosion (n) /ɪk'spləʊʒn/
garden (n) /'gɑːdn/
popularity (n) /pɒpju'lærəti/
reputation (n) /repju'teɪʃn/
shipwreck (n) /'ʃɪprek/
square (n) /skweə(r)/
tank (n) /tæŋk/

Unit 8

carve (v) /kɑːv/
dancer (n) /'dɑːnsə(r)/
decorated (adj) /'dekəreɪtɪd/
fur (n) /fɜː(r)/
prehistoric (adj) /priːhɪ'stɒrɪk/
rock (n) /rɒk/
spray (n) /spreɪ/
stick (n) /stɪk/
work of art (n) /ˌwɜːk əv 'ɑːt/

Starter unit

Comparing
much   better than ... .
a bit / a lot   more interesting
    than ... .
not   as interesting as ... .
twice / three times   as good as
    ... .

Time words
... on Thursdays / Thursday
    evenings.
... at the weekend / at night / at
    (about) seven o'clock.
... in the morning / afternoon /
    evening.
... once or twice a day / week /
    month.
... every Friday.

Unit 1

Comparing opinions
In my opinion, (there are a lot).
I think (the answer is a).
I agree with you.
I don't agree.
I think so, too.
I'm not sure.
I don't think so.

Talking about news
You look happy / fed up /
    pleased.
I've got some amazing / good /
    bad / terrible news.
Really?
Tell me all about it.
What happened?
You're kidding!
That's good news.
What's your news?

Writing a news item
The incident happened (late
    yesterday afternoon).
People were (sleeping) and ... .
There was no ... and there
    weren't ... .
This was the dramatic scene ... .
Later, one of them said, ...

Unit 2

Saying numbers
One point three.
A hundred and one.
Fourteen thousand, five hundred
    and forty.
Thirty-two thousand, nine
    hundred and eight.

A hundred and twenty-five
    thousand.
Two million.

Offering and asking for help
Do you want me to help you with
    anything?
I'd really appreciate it if you don't
    mind.
Shall I get a few cartons of juice
    or something?
Do you mind?
If you want, I can get a bag of ice,
    too.
Could you get some?
OK, no problem, I'll see what
    they've got.

Writing an email
I'm writing because ... .
This photo shows ... .
I think there are possibly (two)
    reasons for this.
Firstly, ... Secondly, ...
We must do something about ... .

Unit 3

Experiences
Have you ever ... ?
What about you?
Yes, occasionally.
Yes, a lot of times.
No, never.
Yes, a few times.
Yes, once (or twice).

Apologizing and making excuses
What is it?
What's the matter?
I'm afraid ... .
I didn't mean to.
I don't know how it happened.
I'm really sorry.
Don't worry.
It won't happen again.

Opinion phrases
... in my experience ... .
... from what I've seen ... .
I think ... .
The problem is that ... .
For this reason, I think ... .
In my opinion, ...

Unit 4

Describing people
She tends to be (quite) ... .
He can be (very) ... .
He's sometimes / always (a bit)
    ... .

He isn't (very) ... .
My (aunt) can be (incredibly) ... .

Talking about qualities
He's / She's quite / very / not
    exactly ... .
He / She has / hasn't got (a lot
    of) ... .
You need (a lot of) ... .
You don't need (much) ... to be a
    (singer).
It's important for a (tennis player)
    to be ... .
A (sports) star needs / doesn't
    need to be ... .

Identifying people
Who's that guy / girl over there?
I think I've seen him / her before.
The guy / girl with long hair.
What about him / her?
Do you know him / her?
He / She looks like someone
    famous.

A biography
She's got ... and ... .
In the years that followed, ...
She's been involved in ... since ... .
... was born in ... .
Since then, she has ... .
Her big break came in ... .

Unit 5

Agreeing and disagreeing
I (don't) think that ... .
I agree / disagree with that / you.
That's right.
I (don't) think so.
I'm not sure about that.
Yes, I think you're right.
That's true, but ... .

Asking for and giving advice
What's the matter?
What should I do?
Whatever you do, don't ... .
That's for sure.
I think you should ... .
Are you sure?

Expressing opinions
I'm (not) in favour of ... .
I'm against ... .
In my opinion / view, ... for two /
    several / various reasons.
All in all, ...
In conclusion, ...
I think that it's a good / bad thing
    to ... .

Unit 6

Making suggestions
Let's (organize a meeting).
That isn't a bad idea.
That should / could / might help a bit.
How about (starting an email campaign)?
I think we should try ... .
Why don't we (boycott the shops)?
That will definitely work better.
I think the best thing to do is ... .
We could write to the council.

Donating money
Have you got a minute?
What can I do for you?
What's it for?
It's for (a children's charity).
I hope to raise about (£150).
It sounds like a good cause.

Formal letters
In our opinion, ...
I represent ... .
For this reason, ...
On the other hand, ...
We have therefore decided to ... .

Unit 7

Expressing likes and dislikes
Would you like to ... ?	Do you like ... ?
Yes, I would.	Yes, I do.
No, I wouldn't.	No, I don't.
I'd love / hate it.	I love / hate it.
I wouldn't mind.	I don't mind.

Recommending and responding
What about this one?
I'd only recommend that if ... .
I don't fancy that.
If they had (*Avatar*), I'd recommend that.
You might like ... .
I'm not a big fan of ... .
Try this one.

Facts and opinions
I have recently read ... .
I'd like to recommend ... .
The main characters are ... .
The setting is ... .
I particularly enjoyed ... .
All in all, I (really enjoyed) ... .
I'd / I wouldn't change it.

Unit 8

Doing a quiz

What's your next question?
OK, you start.
I think the answer's ... .
That's right. Well done.
No, sorry. Bad luck.
OK. It's your turn.

Describing art
It reminds me of ... .
It doesn't look like a ... .
What on earth is that?
I'm not sure about ... .
It looks (a bit mad).
It looks as if (a child painted it).

Describing a painting
The scenery / composition includes ... .
... in the foreground / background ... .
(*The Persistence of Memory*) was first exhibited ... .
It is said that ... .
This type of work is typical of ... .
Their work sometimes shows ... .

Extra listening and speaking

Unit 1

Discussing what to watch
What time is it on?
What's on tonight?
What else is on?
I (don't) fancy watching ... .
Is there a ... on?

Unit 2

Asking about things in a shop
Can I help you?
I need something for ... .
Is this what you mean?
You use it for ... .
Which type do you want?

Unit 3

Saying website and email addresses
www = double u, double u, double u
. = dot
_ = underscore
@ = at
- = hyphen
/ = forward slash
That's all one word.

Unit 4

Describing people
I recognize the name.
I can't picture him.
What does she look like?
I know who you mean.
Isn't he ... ?

Unit 5

Talking about problems at school
Is there a problem with ... ?
There's been a problem in my school with ... .
How do you feel about ... ?
How do you think your school can improve?
We should definitely ... .

Unit 6

Interviewing a campaigner
Why are you campaigning?
What does your placard say?
Can you explain how you feel about ... ?
What are you hoping to achieve?

Unit 7

Talking about films
Which film have you just been to see?
Who's in it?
What did you think of ... ?
Who would you recommend it to?
I'd recommend it to ... .

Unit 8

Talking about a picture
What's it a picture of?
Who was it painted by?
Can you see the ... ?
... at the top / bottom ... .
... on the right / left ... .

	Past simple	Past participle
be /biː, bɪ/	was /wɒz, wəz/, were /wɜː(r), wə(r)/	been /biːn/
become /bɪˈkʌm/	became /bɪˈkeɪm/	become /bɪˈkʌm/
begin /bɪˈgɪn/	began /bɪˈgæn/	begun /bɪˈgʌn/
bite /baɪt/	bit /bɪt/	bitten /ˈbɪtn/
break /breɪk/	broke /brəʊk/	broken /ˈbrəʊkən/
bring /brɪŋ/	brought /brɔːt/	brought /brɔːt/
build /bɪld/	built /bɪlt/	built /bɪlt/
burn /bɜːn/	burnt / burned /bɜːnt, bɜːnd/	burnt / burned /bɜːnt, bɜːnd/
buy /baɪ/	bought /bɔːt/	bought /bɔːt/
can /kæn/	could /kʊd/	
catch /kætʃ/	caught /kɔːt/	caught /kɔːt/
choose /tʃuːz/	chose /tʃəʊz/	chosen /ˈtʃəʊzn/
come /kʌm/	came /keɪm/	come /kʌm/
cut /kʌt/	cut /kʌt/	cut /kʌt/
do /duː/	did /dɪd/	done /dʌn/
drink /drɪŋk/	drank /dræŋk/	drunk /drʌŋk/
drive /draɪv/	drove /drəʊv/	driven /ˈdrɪvn/
eat /iːt/	ate /eɪt, et/	eaten /ˈiːtn/
fall /fɔːl/	fell /fel/	fallen /ˈfɔːlən/
find /faɪnd/	found /faʊnd/	found /faʊnd/
fly /flaɪ/	flew /fluː/	flown /fləʊn/
forget /fəˈget/	forgot /fəˈgɒt/	forgotten /fəˈgɒtn/
get /get/	got /gɒt/	got /gɒt/
get up /ˌget ˈʌp/	got up /ˌgɒt ˈʌp/	got up /ˌgɒt ˈʌp/
give /gɪv/	gave /geɪv/	given /ˈgɪvn/
go /gəʊ/	went /went/	gone /gɒn/
have /hæv/	had /hæd/	had /hæd/
hide /haɪd/	hid /hɪd/	hidden /ˈhɪdn/
hurt /hɜːt/	hurt /hɜːt/	hurt /hɜːt/
keep /kiːp/	kept /kept/	kept /kept/
know /nəʊ/	knew /njuː/	known /nəʊn/
learn /lɜːn/	learnt / learned /lɜːnt, lɜːnd/	learnt / learned /lɜːnt, lɜːnd/
leave /liːv/	left /left/	left /left/
lose /luːz/	lost /lɒst/	lost /lɒst/
make /meɪk/	made /meɪd/	made /meɪd/
meet /miːt/	met /met/	met /met/
put /pʊt/	put /pʊt/	put /pʊt/
read /riːd/	read /red/	read /red/
ride /raɪd/	rode /rəʊd/	ridden /ˈrɪdn/
run /rʌn/	ran /ræn/	run /rʌn/
say /seɪ/	said /sed/	said /sed/
see /siː/	saw /sɔː/	seen /siːn/
send /send/	sent /sent/	sent /sent/
sing /sɪŋ/	sang /sæŋ/	sung /sʌŋ/
sit /sɪt/	sat /sæt/	sat /sæt/
sleep /sliːp/	slept /slept/	slept /slept/
speak /spiːk/	spoke /spəʊk/	spoken /ˈspəʊkən/
spend /spend/	spent /spent/	spent /spent/
swim /swɪm/	swam /swæm/	swum /swʌm/
take /teɪk/	took /tʊk/	taken /ˈteɪkən/
teach /tiːtʃ/	taught /tɔːt/	taught /tɔːt/
tell /tel/	told /təʊld/	told /təʊld/
think /θɪŋk/	thought /θɔːt/	thought /θɔːt/
throw /θrəʊ/	threw /θruː/	thrown /θrəʊn/
understand /ˌʌndəˈstænd/	understood /ˌʌndəˈstʊd/	understood /ˌʌndəˈstʊd/
wear /weə(r)/	wore /wɔː(r)/	worn /wɔːn/
win /wɪn/	won /wʌn/	won /wʌn/
write /raɪt/	wrote /rəʊt/	written /ˈrɪtn/